A*
GCSE
BIOLOGY

THE MANCHESTER GRAMMAR SCHOOL

OXFORD

UNIVERSITY PRESS

OXFORD
UNIVERSITY PRESS

Great Clarendon Street, Oxford OX2 6DP

Oxford University Press is a department of the University of Oxford.
It furthers the University's objective of excellence in research, scholarship,
and education by publishing worldwide in

Oxford New York

Athens Auckland Bangkok Bogotá Buenos Aires Calcutta
Cape Town Chennai Dar es Salaam Delhi Florence Hong Kong Istanbul
Karachi Kuala Lumpur Madrid Melbourne Mexico City Mumbai
Nairobi Paris São Paulo Singapore Taipei Tokyo Toronto Warsaw
with associated companies in Berlin Ibadan

Oxford is a registered trade mark of Oxford University Press
in the UK and in certain other countries

British Library Cataloguing in Publication Data
Data available

ISBN 0 19 914742 6 (school edition)
      0 19 914748 5 (bookshop edition)

Many thanks to Nick Rose, Lee Khvat, Jordan Mayo, Arunabha Ghosh, and Adrian Turner

Typeset by Advance Typesetting Limited, Long Hanborough, Oxon
Printed in Great Britain

preface

The idea for the book which you are now reading came from a group of pupils at The Manchester Grammar School. Their year achieved what some league tables at least reckoned were the best GCSE grades in the country, yet they had found a dearth of good revision guides aimed specifically at able students. They thought they could do better, and the result (as part of the Young Enterprise Scheme) was the best-selling *Physics A* GCSE Revision Guide – written by the students for the students*. The rest, as they say, is history … . The three Guides in this new series produced by the Oxford University Press are written by the same type of people who actually sit GCSEs – the candidates. They are wholly user-friendly, and we hope also that they are exciting in a way few other revision guides can achieve.

    I hope you enjoy working with them as much as all of us here have enjoyed being involved in their production. Royalties from these books go to The Manchester Grammar School Foundation Bursary Fund, which pays for pupils whose parents have low incomes to attend the School; thank you for your help.

Martin Stephen

Dr Martin Stephen
High Master
Manchester Grammar School

contents

the organisation of living things

The characteristics of living things

There are seven characteristics that all living things (except aliens) display:

1. They move.
2. They **respire**. (This is the process of obtaining energy from food.)
3. They grow.
4. They are sensitive to stimuli. (Stimuli are events or conditions in the outside world.)
5. They feed.
6. They **excrete**. (This means getting rid of poisonous waste.)
7. They **reproduce**.

Cells – the building blocks of life

All substances are made of atoms – 'the building blocks of matter'. The 'building blocks of life' are **cells**. The features of typical animal and plant cells are shown in the diagrams.

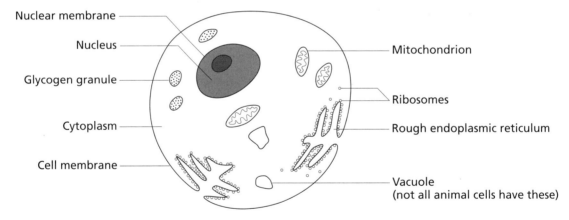

A typical animal cell

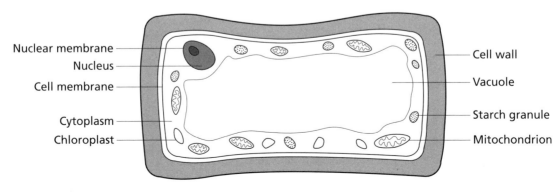

A typical plant cell

What's in a cell?

All cells have a thin film around them called the **cell membrane**. It holds the contents of the cell in. It also controls what goes into and out of the cell – it is **partially permeable**. (If it was fully permeable, nasty stuff might get inside the cell, and important stuff might leak out.) Partially permeable and **selectively permeable** mean the same thing.

The cell membrane contains **carrier proteins**. These are proteins that help the cell to take in things it particularly needs by **active transport** (see topic two).

The cell membrane also has proteins called **receptors** which act like labels for identification. Hormones only interact with cells that have the correct receptor on their membrane.

Proteins on the membrane also label cells as belonging to that organism. The immune system can identify foreign cells because they have an unfamiliar marker protein. (This is one of the problems with transplanted organs. The recipient's immune system will attack the donated organ because it has an unfamiliar marker protein, causing it to be rejected. The patient is given drugs that *suppress* the immune system so that this doesn't happen.) Marker proteins and receptors allow **cell-to-cell recognition**.

The cell is full of a jelly-like substance called **cytoplasm**. Actually, the cytoplasm contains mostly water – 70% – and lots of other substances, especially proteins.

*(**Protoplasm** is a collective term for the contents of a cell.)*

Cells have lots of bits called **organelles**. The one you can see most clearly is the **nucleus**. It is like the 'brain' of the cell, controlling all its functions. (Going back to the atom idea, the central part of the atom is also called the nucleus.) The nucleus contains the **chromosomes**. These control the characteristics of the organism itself. (You can only see the chromosomes when the cell is going to divide.)

The nucleus is wrapped in its own membrane called the **nuclear membrane** (seems logical).

There are lots more membranes in the cell: a whole maze of them runs right through the cytoplasm. This is the **endoplasmic reticulum** (a long name for a large set of membranes). The membrane is *inside* the cell, hence *endo*plasmic. There are bead-like structures on the endoplasmic reticulum called **ribosomes**. (There are some of these loose in the cytoplasm too.) Proteins are made in the ribosomes.

Also in the cytoplasm are the **mitochondria** (singular: **mitochondrion**). This is where **aerobic respiration** happens, producing energy for the cell (more about this in topic six). Mitochondria can be described as the '**power houses**' of the cell.

How are animal and plant cells different?

There are four major differences between animal and plant cells.

- Plant cells are surrounded by a **cell wall**, which is made of **cellulose** fibres criss-crossed to make a strong, rubbery wall. The cell wall gives the cells *protection* and *support* (see page 114). The cell wall is fully permeable, but the cell membrane (which you will remember is partially permeable) is just inside the cell wall.

- Plant cells contain a large **vacuole**, pushing all the cytoplasm and organelles to the edges of the cell. The vacuole contains **cell sap**, which is a solution of salts and sugars dissolved in water. The vacuole also helps to support the cell (see page 13).

  Animal cells sometimes have vacuoles but these are very small and difficult to see. These vacuoles contain 'food' and water (although the food is obviously in a very different form to when it was eaten).

- Most plant cells contain lots of green bits called **chloroplasts**. They are green because they contain **chlorophyll**. Chlorophyll absorbs sunlight, which is essential for **photosynthesis**. (More about this in topic six if you're feeling keen.)

- The sugars that are made in plant cells during photosynthesis are converted into **starch**. This is stored in **granules**.

  Animal cells *never* contain starch. Some animal cells contain **glycogen** which is a long carbohydrate molecule made of sugars, a bit like starch. Glycogen is stored in animal cells as granules.

Plant cells are *regular* in shape because of their cell walls, whereas animal cells are *irregular* in shape. Also, plant cells are usually bigger than animal cells because they contain a vacuole.

A summary of this cell business

The similarities
Plant and animal cells have the following features in common:

- cell membrane
- cytoplasm
- nucleus and nuclear membrane
- mitochondria
- endoplasmic reticulum and ribosomes.

The differences

	Animal cell	*Plant cell*
Cell wall	No	Yes
Chloroplasts	No	Yes
Vacuole	Small (or none)	Large; contains cell sap
Sugar storage	Glycogen granules	Starch granules
Shape	Irregular	Regular

Division of labour

Most organisms are **multicellular**, that is they are made up of lots of cells. The body of an organism is divided into different areas. Each area does a share of the organism's work. The cells in each area are **specialised**. This means that they do one particular job. The structure of the cell suits its particular function and particular chemical processes might occur inside the cell.

The specialisation of each type of cell to carry out a particular function is **division of labour**. The organelles inside the cell also have particular functions, so this is also division of labour. You will come across many examples of specialisation in biology.

Examples of specialised cells

Animals	Plants
• Muscle cells for movement	• Palisade cells for photosynthesis (see page 44)
• Neurones (nerve cells) for conducting impulses (see page 92)	• Root hair cells for absorbing water
• Red blood cells for carrying oxygen (see page 64)	• Guard cells for controlling the opening and closing of stomata (see page 70)

Tissues and organs

Just to recap: what is the smallest part of a living body? The building blocks of life are cells (although you could argue that cells are made up of organelles, which are made up of molecules, which in turn are made up of atoms ...).

* A group of specialised cells forms a **tissue**. For example, the layer of cells in the stomach lining is a tissue.

* Different tissues together form an **organ**. For example, the stomach is an organ made up of different tissues.

* A particular group of organs is a **system**. For example, the stomach is one organ in the digestive system.

* An organism is made up of systems.

So, it goes:

| Cells | → | Tissues | → | Organs | → | Systems | → | Organism |

Worked questions

Q1. *Explain the fact that plant cells have a cell wall and a large cell vacuole, whereas animal cells do not?*

A1.   Plants don't have a skeleton so they need strong cell walls and large vacuoles to provide support and structure. The vacuole is full of water so that the cells push against each other – this is called turgor. Animals get support and structure from a physical skeleton, so individual cells don't have to be so strong.

Also plants are autotrophs – they make their own organic molecules. The sugar they make is stored in the cell sap in the vacuole and is used for respiration and to make proteins and carbohydrates like cellulose. Animals are heterotrophs – they take in complex materials and break them down. They have special tissues for storage and more complex transport systems than plants. This means that individual cells don't have to store as much so animal cells only have a small vacuole for storage. (Some animal cells don't have a vacuole.)

Q2.   *How do cells control which substances enter and leave the cell and what role does the cell wall play in this process?*

A2.   Cells are surrounded by a partially permeable membrane, which only lets certain molecules through. There are also carrier proteins in the membrane which take up specific substances and move them across the membrane by active transport.

The cell wall is fully permeable so it does not play any part in controlling what enters or leaves the cell.

Q3.   *Why is cell-to-cell recognition so important in the body and how is this achieved?*

A3.   Cell-to-cell recognition is important in the action of hormones. Hormones are released into the blood stream but they only interact with the cells that have the right marker protein (called a receptor) on their membranes. This makes sure that they act on the right cells. Cell-to-cell recognition is also important in the immune system. White blood cells attack any cells that don't have the right marker on their cell membrane.

Q4.   *What gives plants their green colour and why is this molecule not present in animal cells?*

A4.   Plants are green because they contain lots of the green pigment called chlorophyll. Chlorophyll traps energy from the sunlight for photosynthesis, the process by which plants make sugars for respiration. (They are autotrophs.) Animals obtain sugar for respiration by breaking down complex carbohydrates that they eat. They do not photosynthesise, so they do not need chlorophyll.

Q5.   *In cells in which the rate of respiration is normally high, which organelle would you expect to find in abundance? Why?*

A5.   The organelles responsible for respiration are mitochondria, and therefore where the rate of respiration is normally high, there needs to be a lot of mitochondria. The mitochondria contain the enzymes involved in respiration and the production of ATP which is how energy is stored for use by the cell.

diffusion, osmosis & active transport

Diffusion

Diffusion   the net movement of particles from an area of high concentration to an area of low concentration

Okay, that's the definition. This is how it works. Molecules in a gas or liquid move **randomly** (randomly is the important part). A molecule is equally likely to move in any direction.

If you have lots of molecules of a gas (for example) in one place, the gas is in **high concentration**. Molecules of the gas are *more likely* to move from the area of high concentration to one of low concentration than in the opposite direction. The **net movement** is therefore down the **concentration gradient**; from high to low concentration. Eventually, all the molecules will be spread out evenly (there is no concentration gradient), so there is no more *net* movement.

As an example, imagine some hydrogen sulphide gas (a rotten-egg smell) released in the corner of a room. At first it is in a high concentration. Molecules of hydrogen sulphide *diffuse* from the corner out into the rest of the room (along the concentration gradient) and more and more people can smell the gas. Eventually, the hydrogen sulphide will diffuse through the entire room. (Whether or not someone has to hold their nose depends on whether the final concentration in the room is enough to cause a smell.)

Diffusion is a physical process which depends on the energy of the molecules.

- Diffusion gets faster as the temperature increases. (This is because the random motion of the molecules increases.)

- Small molecules diffuse more quickly than large molecules.

- The steeper the concentration gradient, the quicker the diffusion.

- Diffusion is slower in water than in air. This gives rise to the need for special transport systems (topic eight): the blood in animals; the xylem and phloem in plants.

Why is diffusion important?

The diffusion of small molecules (e.g. oxygen, carbon dioxide, water) along concentration gradients allows cells to obtain things they need and to get rid of waste products. We can take gaseous exchange as an example:

- In a leaf exposed to sunlight, the cells use carbon dioxide (CO_2) for photosynthesis. This means that there is a lower concentration of CO_2 inside the leaf than outside it. So, the net movement of CO_2 will be through the stomata, into the leaf – diffusion down the concentration gradient.

- Oxygen is produced by cells in the leaf so there is a high oxygen concentration inside and a low concentration outside the leaf. So, the net movement of oxygen is through the stomata, *out* of the leaf – diffusion down the concentration gradient.

- In animals, CO_2 is a waste product that cells need to excrete. It is in a high concentration in the cells where it is produced during aerobic respiration. It diffuses down the concentration gradient into the blood (where it is in lower concentration), which carries the CO_2 away.

- When the blood reaches the lungs, the CO_2 is in a higher concentration in the blood than in the alveoli. The CO_2 therefore diffuses down the concentration from the blood to the alveoli; it is then exhaled.

Osmosis

Osmosis   the diffusion of water across a partially permeable membrane from an area of high water concentration to an area of low water concentration

Make sure you know that definition; with so many long words it's bound to come up in the exam!

Here is an example.

Imagine you have a large beaker in which there is a thin-film balloon containing a solution of purple dye. There are very tiny holes in the membrane of the balloon (no ordinary balloon); the holes are too small to allow the purple dye to pass through but are large enough for water molecules to pass through. The film balloon can be described as a **partially permeable** membrane.

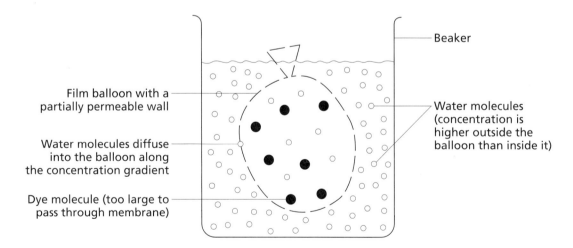

Diffusion of water molecules by osmosis across a partially permeable membrane

The concentration of water is higher outside the balloon than inside it. The water diffuses down the concentration gradient (across the partially permeable membrane) into the balloon, making it swell up. This movement of water is **osmosis**.

*(The idea of 'water concentration' is rather strange. You can also use the term 'water **potential**' rather than water concentration. This is the tendency of water to leave a solution. A solution with a high water potential is one containing a high concentration of water molecules.)*

Remember that osmosis is really a special case of diffusion, describing the net movement of water molecules.

Osmosis in action

One of the purposes of the cell membrane is to separate the cytoplasm from the solution surrounding the cell. Don't forget that the cell membrane is partially permeable; plant cell walls are fully permeable. If the concentrations of water are different inside and outside a cell, osmosis is bound to occur.

Imagine that you use a pipette to add a few drops of distilled water onto an animal cell (e.g. a red blood cell) on a slide. What happens? The cell bursts, of course, because of the net movement of water into the cell by osmosis.

Does the same happen to a plant cell? Yes and no! Water diffuses into the cell by osmosis (as with the red blood cell). However, the cell wall prevents the plant cell from bursting. The cell swells – it becomes **turgid** – and the cell membrane is pushed against the cell wall.

Now think of the opposite situation: what happens if you put the cells in a concentrated salt (or sugar) solution?

In both animal and plant cells, water moves *out* of the cell by osmosis because the water concentration is higher inside the cell than outside it. Remember that the salt (or sugar) molecules are prevented from diffusing into the cell along the concentration gradient by the partially permeable cell membrane.

The animal cell would shrink and soon die. The plant cell would become **flaccid** (the opposite of turgid) and the cell membrane would start to peel away from the cell wall. This is called **plasmolysis** and the cell is said to be **plasmolysed**.

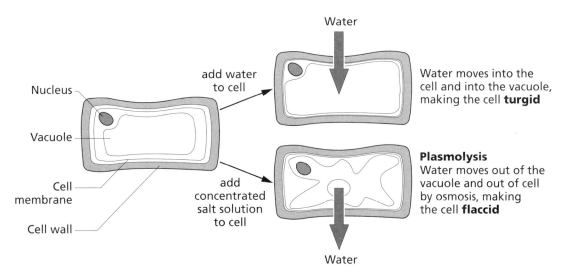

Turgor: the effect of osmosis on plant cells

(The diffusion of water into and out of guard cells by osmosis controls the opening and closing of stomata in leaves [see page 70].)

Active transport

So far we have only talked about the movement of substances into and out of cells by diffusion along a concentration gradient. Organisms cannot always depend on this natural flow of substances from place to place for things it needs. Sometimes substances must be taken into a cell *against* the concentration gradient, that is, from an area of low concentration to an area of high concentration. This process is called **active transport**.

Active transport is dependent on **energy** from respiration (hence the term 'active') and on **carrier proteins** that transport substances across the cell membrane.

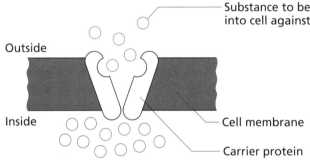

a) *The substance combines with the carrier molecule.*

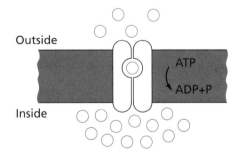

b) *The carrier protein transports the substance across the membrane, possibly by changing shape. This uses energy from respiration.*

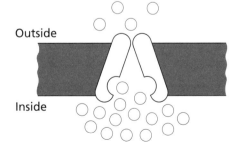

c) *The substance is released into the cell.*

Active transport of a substance across the cell membrane

Active transport   the movement of substances against a concentration gradient using energy from respiration

Some examples of active transport

Consider a root tip in the soil. The plant needs to take up minerals (e.g. nitrate or potassium) from the soil but their concentration is higher in the root than in the soil. If diffusion was the only process, minerals would diffuse out of the plant into the soil. Obviously this isn't what happens! The cells in the root hair have carrier proteins in their membranes. These proteins can 'hold' the minerals that are needed and take them into the cell.

Glucose is taken up into liver cells (where it is converted to glycogen for storage) from the blood by active transport.

Sodium ions are expelled from nerve cells (neurones) by active transport. This maintains the concentration gradient across the cell membrane, needed for conduction of impulses.

Worked questions

Q1.   How could you increase the rate of diffusion?

A1.   You can increase the rate of diffusion by:
   a)   making the concentration gradient steeper (a bigger difference between the maximum and minimum concentrations)
   b)   increasing the surface area over which it occurs
   c)   decreasing the distance over which it occurs
   d)   increasing the temperature to make the particles move faster
   e)   maintaining the concentration gradient by removing the substance from the area with the lower concentration.

Q2.   Explain the motion of the particles, once the concentration gradient has levelled out.

A2.   Once the concentration gradient has levelled out, the particles will still be moving about randomly but the movement in one direction will be cancelled by movement in the opposite direction. This means that there is no net movement of the substance and its concentration stays evened out.

Q3.   Explain in terms of water molecules how a plant cell becomes plasmolysed and on the other hand turgid.

A3.   Water molecules move via osmosis, which is the diffusion of water across a partially permeable membrane from an area of higher water concentration to one which is lower.

   If a plant cell is placed in a strong sugar solution, the concentration of water is higher inside the cell than outside. Water diffuses out of the cell by osmosis. This causes the cell membrane to pull away from the cell wall as the vacuole empties – this is plasmolysis.

If a plant cell is put in water, the concentration of water is higher outside than inside the cell, so water moves into the vacuole of the cell by osmosis. This makes the cell swell, but the cell wall prevents it from bursting. The cell is said to be turgid.

Q4. *How do plant root cells absorb minerals from the soil, against a concentration gradient?*

A4. Plant root cells absorb minerals from the soil via active transport, against a concentration gradient. Specific carrier proteins in the cell membrane recognise essential mineral ions and carry these into the cell by changing shape. This process uses energy.

Q5. *As the rate of active transport increases, how would you expect it to affect the rate of respiration? Explain your answer.*

A5. Active transport requires energy in order for the carrier proteins to move the required molecules into the cell. This energy is provided by respiration. Therefore as the rate of active transport increases, the rate of respiration must increase, in order to supply the increasing demand for energy.

enzymes

Lots of reactions take place inside cells. In living organisms, chemical reactions are sometimes called **metabolic reactions**. **Photosynthesis**, for example, is a metabolic reaction: water and carbon dioxide are converted to glucose and oxygen. But, sparkling water is just water and carbon dioxide. If you leave a bottle of sparkling water on its own even for a billion years, it is unlikely to transform into glucose and oxygen. Something speeds the reaction up in photosynthesis: a **catalyst**, sort of. You may have heard about catalysts in chemistry; they speed up reactions without being used up themselves. Something similar is involved in biological reactions: a **biological catalyst**. These are called **enzymes**; they **catalyse** biological reactions. Enzymes both speed up and *control* metabolic reactions, making sure the right reactions happen in the right place and at the right time.

Each enzyme is designed to catalyse a different reaction, or part of a reaction. But what is it about an enzyme that makes is **specific** to a particular reaction? It's its *shape*. Enzymes are *three-dimensional proteins*. The shape of each kind of enzyme is very precise.

You can take some hydrogen peroxide and let it break down to water and oxygen. In chemistry you could speed up the reaction by adding some manganese(IV) oxide.

Hydrogen peroxide is a waste product in the liver. It is very poisonous so it must be broken down very quickly. **Catalase** is an enzyme that catalyses the breakdown of hydrogen peroxide, essentially performing the same function as the manganese(IV) oxide. Catalase works very quickly: one catalase molecule can convert six million molecules of hydrogen peroxide into water and oxygen in a minute!

Enzymes are very specific; catalase is useless for any reaction other than the breakdown of hydrogen peroxide.

How enzymes work

Obviously this is only a diagram because enzymes don't really look like the letter E for Enzyme!

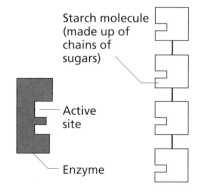

Starch molecule (made up of chains of sugars)

Active site

Enzyme

a) *The enzyme has a very specific three-dimensional shape. The molecule on which the enzyme acts (e.g. starch) is called the **substrate**. The part of the enzyme into which the substrate fits is called the **active site**. The active site is shaped specifically for the enzyme's substrate. This is sometimes called the **lock and key** model: each lock has a specific key that unlocks it.*

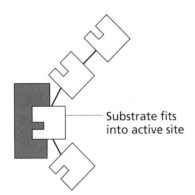

Substrate fits
into active site

b) *The substrate fits into the active site, and the enzyme splits the starch molecule up.*

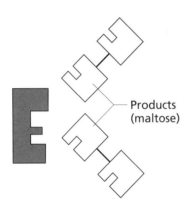

Products
(maltose)

c) *The **products** (in this case maltose) formed are released from the active site; the enzyme is left unchanged and can catalyse another reaction.*

Of course this is only one type of reaction: breaking down of starch. There is another enzyme that builds up starch from the glucose formed in photosynthesis. (An enzyme that does this is called **starch phosphorylase**.)

> *(Names for certain special enzymatic reactions:*
> * *Hydrolysis – breaking down [by adding water]*
> * *Condensation – building up [by taking water away].)*

Enzymes and temperature

Enzymes work faster as the temperature increases – but only to a certain point. This is because as you heat a reaction up, the particles move faster. This means that there is more chance of a substrate molecule bumping into the active site of an enzyme, so the rate of reaction increases.

In all enzyme-controlled reactions there is a maximum temperature at which the enzymes can work. Because enzymes are proteins, they are **denatured** at high temperatures (usually above about 40°C). This means that their structure is changed so they are no longer the right shape for the reaction they catalyse. (It is wrong to say that enzymes are killed, because they are not living organisms.)

> *(In some [but certainly not all] biological [but not necessarily chemical] reactions, the rate of reaction approximately doubles with every 10°C rise in temperature. [This is only true if the reaction has a typical **activation energy** (you don't need to worry about this until A level) and over a typical temperature range.])*

Summary: properties of enzymes

1. They are all proteins, with specific three-dimensional shapes.

2. They are catalysts, and remain unchanged after the reaction. They can therefore be used again and again.

3. Enzymes are specific: they will only catalyse a particular reaction, because of the shape of their active site.

4. Enzymes are denatured and stop working at high temperatures.

5. Enzymes work best at a very specific pH. For example, pepsin works best at pH 3. Most enzymes work best at about pH 7; they are often denatured by extreme acid or alkaline conditions.

Uses of enzymes

- The washing powder you use may say 'biological' on the packet. It contains **proteases** (protein-digesting enzymes) and **lipases** (fat-digesting enzymes). These digest fat and protein stains, which are then washed away.

  A blood stain, for example, contains the protein haemoglobin. Once this is digested, only colourless soluble compounds are left, which are washed away.

  Some proteases can work at the high temperatures inside a washing machine (above 40°C) without being denatured, and they allow the other parts of the washing powder to work.

- Baby foods contain proteases to partially digest the proteins to polypeptides. This helps the baby to digest and absorb the protein in the food.

- There exists in this uncertain Universe a type of sugar called fructose. It is sweeter than glucose, so you need less of it for the same sweetness; this makes it useful for slimming foods. One enzyme that turns glucose into fructose is called **isomerase**.

- It can be very difficult to use enzymes if they are in solution; you have to be able to hold them still (**immobilise** them). You can stick enzymes to beads, for example. (The beads are often made from a substance called **alginate**.) The process of sticking enzymes to things is called **adsorption**. (Be careful to spell this correctly; it's not the same as absorption.)

  If you had a lot of beads with enzymes adsorbed to them, you could drip a solution of the substrate molecule through them. The products would drip out, leaving the enzymes stuck to the beads. This avoids the problem of getting enzymes mixed up with the products. Also, you wouldn't have to put the substrate in a batch at a time; you could leave it dripping through continuously. This is therefore a **continuous process**, as opposed to a **batch process**, where you put in a batch of ingredients, wait for them to react, remove the products, and then add another batch. Most importantly, you can reuse the enzymes, which is one of the most useful things about enzymes anyway.

- Many people who have diabetes use a **biosensor** to measure the level of glucose in their blood. One type is called a **glucose oxidase biosensor**. The tip of the biosensor is made of a gel that has glucose oxidase immobilised in it. If the gel comes into contact with glucose in the blood, oxygen is used up in the reaction catalysed by the glucose oxidase. The change in oxygen level causes a current to flow which is detected by the biosensor. The current is different for different amounts of oxygen being used up, so the biosensor can measure how much glucose there was in the blood.

Biosensors are useful because they are sensitive, specific and give a direct reading.

Worked questions

Q1. *Why does an enzyme only act on a specific substrate?*

A1. Enzymes are three-dimensional proteins. The active site has a very specific shape into which only the correct substrate fits properly so that the enzyme works (in the same way that only the correct key will operate a lock).

Q2. *How can the rate of a reaction using an enzyme be kept at an optimum level?*

A2. An enzyme-controlled reaction can be kept at an optimum rate by maintaining optimum conditions for the enzyme to work at. That is, an optimum temperature, pH and by having an excess of enzyme.

Q3. *Explain how the rate of enzyme action changes as the temperature increases.*

A3. The rate of reaction increases as the temperature increases towards the optimum. This is because the substrate molecules move around more, and are more likely to combine with the active site of the enzyme. The rate of reaction is highest at the optimum temperature and will decrease as the temperature continues to increase above the optimum. Above a certain temperature (about 40°C for human enzymes), the enzyme is denatured: the protein structure is changed so that the substrate no longer fits the active site. The rate of reaction decreases rapidly.

Q4. *Explain, giving two examples, how enzymes are in use in daily life.*

A4. The main use of enzymes today is in biological washing powders, in which proteases and lipases are used to digest protein and fat stains on the clothes.

Secondly baby foods contain proteases which help in the digestion of protein in the food, as babies cannot perform this function to an optimum.

(NB There are lots more possible answers to this question – see previous page.)

Q5. *Explain the advantages of using immobilised enzymes in an industrial process.*

A5. Immobilised enzymes allow continuous rather than batch processing to be used. The substrate is continually added to the enzyme, and the product is collected. The product doesn't need to be separated from the enzyme, and the enzyme is not wasted but can be used lots of times.

Q6. *Explain how a person with diabetes derives benefit from enzymes today.*

A6. Diabetics use a biosensor to measure how much glucose is in their blood. The tip of the biosensor is covered in a gel that has the enzyme glucose oxidase immobilised on it. When the enzyme comes into contact with glucose in the blood, it catalyses a reaction that gives off oxygen. The change in oxygen level is detected by the biosensor as a current. The amount of current is proportional to the concentration of glucose.

nutrition

All living things need food:

- to obtain energy
- for growth
- for repair.

The process of obtaining food is called **nutrition**. There are two types.

Autotrophic nutrition involves taking in simple **inorganic** molecules and using these to form complex substances. Plants are autotrophic organisms (or **autotrophs**): during photosynthesis they build up large complex molecules from small molecules. (We get on to this in topic six.)

Heterotrophic nutrition involves taking in complex **organic** molecules, which are then **digested** to simpler products that are absorbed into the body. Humans and animals are heterotrophic organisms (or **heterotrophs**). The ready-made organic food they eat ultimately comes from green plants. (We get on to digestion in topic five.)

> *(Substances can be classified as:*
>
> - *inorganic, which are simple molecules such as water, minerals, gases*
> - *organic, which are made by living organisms – carbohydrates, fats, proteins, amino acids, DNA, etc.)*

Diet

To remain healthy you need to eat food from certain **food groups** in the right proportions – this is called a **balanced diet**. (The word diet means the food you take in each day, not, as some chat-show hosts may have convinced you, the food you don't take in.)

The main food groups are:

- carbohydrates
- proteins
- fats (lipids)
- vitamins
- minerals
- fibre
- water.

We shall look at each of these in some detail.

Carbohydrates

Chemically, these contain the elements carbon (C), hydrogen (H) and oxygen (O). Hydrogen and oxygen are in the ratio 2H : 1O; hydrogen and carbon are almost in the ratio 2H : 1C. For example, the formula for sucrose (table sugar) is $C_{12}H_{22}O_{11}$.

Animals (including humans) get energy through respiration. Humans get about 17 kilojoules of energy per gram of carbohydrate. You will probably get your carbohydrates from things like bread, potatoes, rice and cakes.

Glucose is an example of a **monosaccharide** – mono for 'one' and saccharide for 'sugar'. A monosaccharide is the simplest form of a carbohydrate. Sucrose is a **disaccharide** – two monosaccharides joined together (in this case, glucose + fructose).

Mono- and disaccharides are called 'simple sugars'. (Although the structural formula of glucose doesn't seem very simple!) They are small, soluble, and taste sweet.

Polysaccharides are long chains of simple sugars. Starch, glycogen and cellulose are all polysaccharides. They are insoluble and they don't taste sweet.

How to test for simple sugars in food
Simple sugars can reduce the copper compounds in **Benedict's solution**.

This is how you do the test:

1. Cut the food into pieces, add water, and dissolve it.

2. Boil it with Benedict's solution.

The colour of the liquid will eventually change from blue to red if there are simple sugars in the food.

Sucrose does not reduce Benedict's solution. This is because it is a disaccharide. You need to break it down into its monosaccharides. To do this, you boil the sucrose with hydrochloric acid, then neutralise it with sodium bicarbonate (Na_2CO_3), (keep adding till the fizzing stops). You then do the Benedict's solution test again.

How to test for starch in food
You can test for starch by adding **iodine solution**. If it changes from a browny yellow to a dark blue or black, starch is present.

Proteins

These contain carbon (C), hydrogen (H), oxygen (O) and nitrogen (N). They sometimes contain phosphorus (P) or sulphur (S).

> *(The symbols of these elements spell CHONPS, which unfortunately isn't a real word, but is quite close to 'chomps'.)*

Proteins are vitally important.

• They are needed to repair tissues and to form new ones.

• Enzymes, hormones and antibodies are all proteins. (You don't need me to tell you how important these are!)

Proteins are not normally used for getting energy but they can be used if *all* other sources have been used up.

Humans get protein from things like milk, fish, eggs, beans and meat (unless you are a vegetarian of course!)

Proteins are made of lots of **amino acids** joined in a long chain. There are 20 different amino acids. They are joined together in lots of different proteins or **polypeptides**.

Peptides are short chains of amino acids; polypeptides are longer chains, and proteins are longer still.

Some proteins are **soluble**, e.g. haemoglobin; some are **insoluble**, e.g. keratin – the stuff hair and fingernails are made of.

Essential amino acids

The body can make some amino acids. The ones that it can't make are called **essential amino acids** because they must be included in the diet. Absence of any one of these can lead to poor health.

Different proteins contain different amino acids. Eggs, meat and fish contain all the essential amino acids. To get the essential amino acids from plant protein, you have to eat a mixture of different proteins, e.g. wheat protein, bean proteins or soya protein. (Beans on toast is a healthy meal!) Obviously this is pretty important for vegetarians.

How to test for proteins in food

1. Put the food in a test tube.

2. Add a little water.

3. Add some sodium or potassium hydroxide solution ($NaOH_{(aq)}$ or $KOH_{(aq)}$).

4. Add two drops of very dilute copper sulphate solution ($CuSO_{4(aq)}$).

If a purple colour is produced on shaking the test tube, protein is present. This is called the **biuret** test.

Fats

Fats contain carbon, hydrogen and oxygen but in a different ratio to carbohydrates.

Fats are primarily used as stores of energy. They produce more energy than carbohydrates: about 39 kilojoules per gram, which is more than twice as much as carbohydrates. However, the reactions are more complex than the ones for breaking down carbohydrates, so the carbohydrates are used first.

Fats are also important for **insulation**. A layer of cells below the skin becomes filled with large drops of fats and oils. This layer is called **adipose tissue**. Animals that live in cold conditions have thick layers of adipose tissue. For example, whales have blubber.

A hard layer of fat protects delicate organs like the kidneys.

Fats are an important source of fat-soluble vitamins (see pages 26–7) and are an essential part of cell membranes.

Fats and oils (**lipids**) are made from **fatty acids** and **glycerol**. One molecule of glycerol combines with three fatty acid molecules to form a **triglyceride**. Lipids are mixtures of triglycerides.

> *(Glycerol is also known as propan-1,2,3-triol, so the chemists among you can figure out what it looks like, if you feel so inclined.)*

You must have heard people going on about **saturated** and **unsaturated** fats. This is quite easy to understand.

• **Saturated** means that the fat cannot combine with any more hydrogen because it doesn't have any double bonds.

• **Monounsaturated** means that the fat has one (hence mono) double bond, so more hydrogen could be added.

• **Polyunsaturated** fats have lots of double bonds, so lots of hydrogen could be added.

A saturated molecule
(no double bonds)

A monounsaturated molecule
(one double bond)

A polyunsaturated molecule
(several double bonds)

These are simple molecular structures to explain saturated and unsaturated. (I'm sure you've noticed that these aren't fats, but the principle is the same.) More hydrogen could be added at the double bonds in the unsaturated molecules.

Animal fats contain a lot of saturated fats (which is why they are solid) whereas plant oils (e.g. olive oil) contain a lot of unsaturated compounds (which is why they are liquid – or have a lower melting point to be more precise).

People make a lot of fuss about different types of fat because scientists think that eating a lot of *saturated* fats increases the risk of **heart disease**. Fat deposits (**cholesterol**) can build up in arteries (this is called **atherosclerosis**), reducing the amount of blood (and therefore oxygen) that gets to the heart or brain. This can cause **heart attacks** or **strokes**.

How to test for fats in food
The grease paper test (unsophisticated method)

Rub some of the substance onto a piece of filter paper. If that area becomes translucent, there are lipids present. However, this tends not to work very well with solid fats; it works better with oils.

The emulsion test (sophisticated method)

1. Fats are soluble in ethanol, so you take the food and dissolve it in ethanol in a test tube.

2. Fats are not soluble in water, so when you add water to the test tube, if fat is present globules will appear, and the water will go cloudy. This is because millions of fat particles come out of solution and form an **emulsion**. (Milk is an emulsion.)

Vitamins

Vitamins are organic substances (they contain carbon). Their chemical structures are completely unrelated to each other. Vitamins are essential in small amounts for normal health. They work with enzymes in chemical reactions. They are not broken down for energy.

The following table tells you about the main vitamins: examples of the food you can get them from, things you need them for, and the **deficiency** state, that is, what happens if there is not enough of the vitamin in your diet.

Vitamin	Source	Why needed	Deficiency disease(s)
A (retinol) (Fat soluble)	Butter, egg yolk, cod-liver oil, milk, cheese Retinol can be made in the body from carotene, which is found in carrots and green leaves	Keeps the lining of the respiratory system in good repair Used to make the pigment in the rod cells of eyes; needed for dim light vision	Infection of cells lining the respiratory system Night blindness
B (There are about 12 different B vitamins but they are usually found together)*	Wholemeal bread, yeast extract (e.g. Marmite), brown rice	Involved in many chemical reactions, e.g. respiration	Beri-beri, which can occur if polished rice is the staple diet, instead of brown rice. It causes muscular weakness and paralysis*

continued:

Vitamin	Source	Why needed	Deficiency disease(s)
C (ascorbic acid)	Oranges, lemons (citrus fruits), blackcurrants, raw vegetables, potatoes	Keeps skin and blood vessels healthy	Scurvy – causes pains in joints and muscles and bleeding gums
D (calciferol) (Fat soluble)	Butter, egg yolk, fish-liver oil; skin can produce it in sunlight	Helps the body to absorb calcium from food and to deposit it in bones	Rickets – causes bones to become soft and deformed; children in industrial areas used to get rickets because they got very little sunshine
E	Egg yolk, milk, green vegetables	Fertility	Lack of it causes the ovaries or testes to wither so sperm or eggs are not produced
K	Spinach, egg yolk, pig's liver; bacteria in the gut also make it	Helps blood to clot	Blood doesn't clot properly

*Niacin (vitamin B3) is found in meat and fish; lack of it causes pellagra, which causes swollen tongues and skin rashes. Vitamin B1 is called thiamine; lack of this causes beri-beri (see above). Vitamin B2 is called riboflavin. It is found in leafy vegetables, eggs and fish. Lack of it causes sores on the skin and around the mouth, and poor growth.

How to do a food test for vitamin C

1. Take some *DCPIP and add the solution of food drop by drop.

2. Count the number of drops needed for the solution to decolorise; the fewer the drops, the more vitamin C there is in the food.

> *(*DCPIP stands for 2,6,dichlorophenolindophenol. [Don't worry, you don't need to learn that ridiculously long name.])*

Minerals

Minerals are **inorganic** substances (unlike vitamins). Again, they are only required in small amounts. Minerals are also referred to as **mineral salts**.

Table salt is **sodium chloride**. Sodium helps nerves to transmit impulses. Lack of it can cause muscle cramp. Sodium is lost by sweating, so people living in hot places may need to take sodium tablets. Too much sodium can cause high blood pressure.

Calcium is found in milk and cheese. Calcium is needed for muscle contraction and for the transmission of nerve impulses. It is also essential for blood clotting. Calcium in the form of **calcium phosphate** is essential for the formation of strong bones and teeth. Vitamin D helps the body to absorb calcium from food.

Phosphorus is essential for strong teeth and bones, and is also needed to make ATP (more about this on page 48). Phosphorus is present in most foods as **phosphates**.

Fluorine seems to harden the enamel of teeth and so prevents tooth decay. It is now present in most drinking water and in fluoride toothpaste.

Iron is an essential part of **haemoglobin**, which is the pigment in red blood cells responsible for carrying oxygen around the body. Iron is also needed by muscles and some enzymes. Red meat, and particularly liver and kidney, are rich sources of iron; you can also get iron from peanuts, eggs and green vegetables such as spinach. Your liver recycles some of the iron from old red blood cells.

If you don't have enough iron you can get **anaemia** – this makes you tired because you don't have enough haemoglobin to carry oxygen around the body.

Iodine is found in vegetables and sea food. It is needed to make **thyroxine** (a hormone produced by the **thyroid gland)**. Lack of iodine causes the thyroid gland in the neck to swell up, because thyroxine cannot be produced. This swelling is called a **goitre**. Lack of thyroxine leads to a slow metabolic rate.

Fibre

Dietary fibre or **roughage** is food material that can't be digested – it is mostly cellulose from plants which, unlike cows and sheep, we don't have enzymes to digest. The fibre goes through the digestive system to the large intestine – the colon – where bacteria can digest some of it to make fatty acids.

The fibre and the bacteria add bulk to the contents of the colon and help it retain water. This makes the **faeces** softer and reduces the time for them to pass through the colon. This keeps the colon healthy and stops you getting **constipation**. Roughage is also thought to help protect against **bowel cancer**.

You get fibre from plants, which contain cellulose and lignin (which we humans can't digest). Brown bread and rice contain much more fibre than the white versions. **Bran** (the husk of cereals) is also a good source of fibre.

Water

Last but by no means least – water is really important!

- Water makes up about 70% of most tissues; it is an essential part of cells' cytoplasm.

- Digested foods, mineral salts and vitamins are carried around in solution in the blood. Also, waste products are excreted from the body in solution (by the kidneys). Water is acting as a **solvent** and **transport medium** in these processes.

- **Digestion** uses water in the chemical reactions that break down food – **hydrolysis** (this is the subject of the next topic).

- Body fluids, blood, lymph and tissue fluid all contain a lot of water.

You lose water by **sweating**, **urination** and **breathing**, so it is essential to drink plenty of water. Water is produced by the body during chemical respiration.

Balanced diets

Your diet must contain a **balance** of the seven food types (you should know what they are by now), that is, in the right **proportions**. No one food provides everything you need, and lack of one element could cause problems.

Energy

Carbohydrates are the best source of energy, followed by fats. (Fats contain more energy but it is more 'expensive' for the body to obtain; carbohydrates are a more efficient source of energy.)

Teenage boys need about 12,000 kilojoules (kJ) of energy each day; girls need a bit less – about 9600 kJ per day.

The energy is needed:

- to keep our body temperature constant
- to do work and other activities
- to keep body functions (breathing, digestion) going.

Different needs at different times

Pregnant women do not necessarily need to eat extra food, as long as they eat a balanced diet. They do need to make sure that they are eating enough protein for the baby's development, calcium and vitamin D for bones, and iron for making haemoglobin. (Women need more haemoglobin while they are pregnant.) **Folic acid** (one of the B vitamins) helps reduce the possibility of birth defects like spina bifida.

Once the baby is born, the woman needs to keep a good intake of protein, calcium and vitamins while she is breastfeeding the baby.

Growing children need more protein as a proportion of their body weight than adults, for making extra tissues. They also need a good supply of calcium and vitamin D for bones, iron for red blood cells, and vitamin A to help resistance to illnesses.

Adolescents also need a lot of protein and energy for growth (and extra energy for being active) and of course the usual vitamins and minerals.

Too much food

We all know that you get fat if you eat too much. If you take in more food than your body needs for energy and growth, the surplus is stored as glycogen in the liver and as adipose tissue – the polite word for fat. You become **overweight** and eventually **obese** (very overweight). Being overweight can cause all sorts of problems like heart disease, high blood pressure and diabetes.

Exercise helps you to use more energy so that your body does not produce so much fat; it also helps you to lose weight.

Too little food

Starvation means a lack of food in general. **Malnutrition** means the lack of a balanced diet. For example, lack of protein leads to **kwashiorkor** (tricky spelling). This is quite common in developing countries in children aged between 9 months and 2 years. It happens when they stop breastfeeding and rice becomes the staple diet. The children are underweight but look fat because their diet is mainly carbohydrate.

Different ways of feeding

So far we have talked about heterotrophic nutrition, particularly in humans. We need to mention some other types of nutrition. (We get on to autotrophic nutrition in plants in topic six.)

Phagocytosis

Some cells feed by **phagocytosis**: they take food particles into a **vacuole**; digestive enzymes are then secreted into the vacuole.

An *Amoeba* finds its prey by moving along a chemical gradient towards the highest concentration of food. It sends out **pseudopodia** (pseudo – false; podia – feet) around the food, forming a vacuole. When it has digested the prey, the undigestible parts are **egested**.

Phagocytes are white blood cells involved in the immune response. They remove bacteria by phagocytosis.

Insects

Insects have a long tube called a proboscis, which is an extension of their 'mouth'. Saliva is injected onto the food via the proboscis; enzymes in the saliva digest the food. The digested food is then sucked up through the proboscis.

Whales

Whales feed by **filter feeding**. They gulp water and force it out through the filter-like plates that descend from the roof of their mouth. These plates trap **plankton**, which are microscopic plants; they form the principal source of food for the whale.

Saprotrophic nutrition

Saprotrophs (also called **saprophytes**) feed on the substance they grow on – dead and decaying matter such as a rotting tree trunk or food.

Fungi (mushrooms, toadstools and moulds) feed by **saprotrophic nutrition**. *Mucor* is a mould that grows on bread. It has many threads called **hyphae** which form a large mesh network, called a **mycelium**. The tips of the hyphae secrete enzymes. *Mucor* digests the starch on bread, turning it into sugars, which diffuse into the hyphae. The hyphae grow into the space left by the dissolved food.

Many bacteria also feed saprotrophically.

Saprotrophs can be useful: they can cause decay, which may release nutrients. However, some saprotrophs are dangerous, and are capable of producing toxins – these can lead to food poisoning, like *salmonella*.

Worked questions

Q1. Compare the chemical components of carbohydrates, proteins and fats.

A1. Carbohydrates, proteins and fats all contain carbon, hydrogen and oxygen. In carbohydrates the ratio is approximately 1C : 2H : 1O. Proteins also contain nitrogen and may contain sulphur or phosphorus.

Q2. Explain how you would carry out Benedict's test on a non-reducing polysaccharide e.g. sucrose, in order to see if its monosaccharides are reducing sugars.

A2. First ensure that the polysaccharide is in solution. Then you split the polysaccharide into its monosaccharides. To do this, add hydrochloric acid and boil for a few minutes. Then add sodium bicarbonate until there is no more fizzing, i.e. when the neutralisation of the acid is complete. Then add Benedict's solution and boil for a further 4–5 minutes. If the monosaccharides are reducing sugars, a brick-red precipitate will appear.

Q3. You are supplied with a liquid solution X containing dissolved food extract. Explain the various tests that could be carried out on this solution in order to test whether or not it contains fats, proteins and reducing sugars.

A3. To test whether the solution contains fat, put a small amount of X in a test tube, add ethanol (to dissolve the fat). Decant this solution into another test tube containing distilled water. If the water turns slightly cloudy, or white globules appear, fats are present.

To test for protein, add a small amount of sodium hydroxide solution to a small amount of X. Add 2 drops of dilute copper sulphate and shake the tube. If the solution turns a lilac colour, protein is present.

To test for reducing sugars, pour a small amount of X into a boiling tube and add Benedict's solution. Boil for 4–5 minutes. If a brick-red precipitate appears, reducing sugars are present.

Q4. *Explain the importance of fats and proteins in the body.*

A4. Fats are important in the body in order to provide insulation, via a layer of fat under the skin. Its other important function is as an energy supply. A layer of hard fat surrounds delicate organs like the kidneys, providing protection. Some vitamins are stored in fat (e.g. A and D).

Proteins are essential for enzymes, haemoglobin, keratin (which is in hair and fingernails) and for muscle structure. Proteins are needed to repair damaged tissue and build new tissues.

Q5. *In the past scurvy was prevalent among sailors. Explain why this was the case, relating it to the lack of a certain vitamin, and how the problem could be overcome.*

A5. Scurvy was caused by a lack of vitamin C because sailors did not get enough fresh vegetables or fruit on the ships. The problem could be overcome simply by consuming citrus fruits on a regular basis. Citrus fruits are rich in vitamin C.

Q6. *Minerals are not only important to plants, they are also essential to the human body. Explain the importance of a healthy calcium and iron intake.*

A6. Calcium is essential for the development of healthy bones and teeth. It is also important in blood clotting, muscle contraction and conduction of nerve impulses.

Iron is essential for haemoglobin, which carries oxygen in red blood cells in the blood. If there is insufficient, anaemia will result, which causes fatigue and lack of energy, because the rate of respiration is hindered.

Q7. *Given the choice of foods containing animal fats or those containing plant fats, which one would you choose, based on health reasons?*

A7. Animal fats are saturated (i.e. no double bonds) whereas plant fats are unsaturated (i.e. double bonds are present). Saturated fats are more likely to cause heart disease than unsaturated fats. I would therefore choose plant fats because they are healthier than animal fats.

For the food that we eat to be useful, it has to be converted into forms that the body can use. This is **digestion**: solid food is **dissolved** and the soluble products are **absorbed** into the blood. (This soluble form is usable, even though it is no longer recognisable.)

Some food particles are already small enough and are in the right form, so they don't need to be digested. These include vitamins, minerals, simple sugars and water.

There are two types of digestion.

Mechanical digestion breaks down large pieces of food into smaller pieces. This increases the surface area of the food for enzymes to work on. **Chewing (mastication)** is an example of mechanical digestion.

Chemical digestion involves enzymes. These change large molecules into small molecules that can be absorbed into the blood.

Teeth

Teeth perform mechanical digestion.

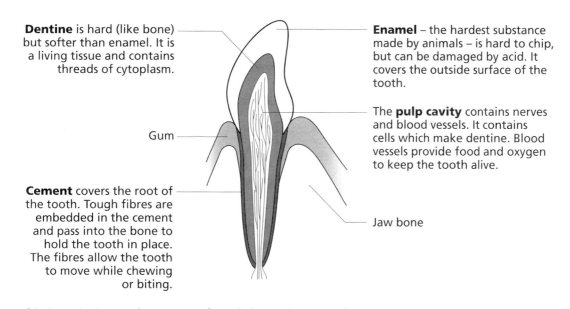

Dentine is hard (like bone) but softer than enamel. It is a living tissue and contains threads of cytoplasm.

Enamel – the hardest substance made by animals – is hard to chip, but can be damaged by acid. It covers the outside surface of the tooth.

Gum

The **pulp cavity** contains nerves and blood vessels. It contains cells which make dentine. Blood vessels provide food and oxygen to keep the tooth alive.

Cement covers the root of the tooth. Tough fibres are embedded in the cement and pass into the bone to hold the tooth in place. The fibres allow the tooth to move while chewing or biting.

Jaw bone

This is an incisor; other types of teeth have the same features.

There are different types of teeth with different functions. At the front of the mouth are the **incisors**; these are chisel shaped, for biting. To their left and right are the **canines**. These are similar to incisors but are more pointed. On either side of the canines, going towards the back of the mouth, are the **premolars** then the **molars**. These have wide surfaces, and are used for grinding.

Milk teeth and permanent teeth

You are born with no teeth – or at least it looks like that but really the teeth are already formed in the gums. The first teeth you get are called **milk teeth** or **deciduous** teeth. These **erupt** (appear) at 3–6 months old. There are 20 altogether: 4 incisors, 2 canines and 4 molars in each jaw bone.

You lose milk teeth from 6–12 years old and they are replaced by the **permanent teeth**. There are 32 of these altogether: 4 incisors, 2 canines, 4 premolars and 6 molars in each jaw. The back molar in each row is called a **wisdom tooth**. These usually grow when you are adult (although some people never grow them). The rest of your permanent teeth have usually grown by 17 years old.

Tooth decay

Bacteria and substances from saliva form **plaque**, which is soft and easy to remove by brushing. It tends to accumulate between the teeth and next to the gums. Plaque hardens and forms **tartar**, which cannot be removed by brushing. If plaque is not removed the bacteria in it will infect the gums. The gums become swollen and inflamed, and bleed on brushing. This may be painless, but bacteria may work down to the root and the tooth is loosened. It may even fall out or need to be removed.

Tooth decay develops when the bacteria in plaque feed on sugar and form acid. This dissolves the enamel (no pain), then the dentine (a little painful), then the pulp cavity (hell-raising pain). At this point, the tooth needs to be removed, or the bacteria can work down to the root and form an abscess.

Different teeth for different diets

Different animals have different types of teeth depending on what they eat.

Herbivores eat plants and grasses. They have the following:

- a tough horny pad instead of incisors on the upper jaw; the incisors in the lower jaw bite against this
- no canine teeth in the upper jaw; the canines in the lower jaw look like incisors
- a space in front of the premolars called the **diastema**. The animal pushes its tongue through this gap to sweep grass into the mouth.
- The premolars and molars have layers of cement, enamel and dentine which wear away at different rates. The ridges that form make a good surface for grinding.

Carnivores eat meat. They have:

- long well-developed canines for grasping and tearing
- powerful jaw muscles
- incisors, premolars and molars for cutting.
- The premolars on each side of the upper jaw and the last molar on each side of the bottom jaw are very large. These are the **carnassial** teeth, which are particularly suited to cutting through flesh and bone.

Omnivores eat meat and plant food. Humans are omnivores. Our dentition is suited to our mixed diet.

Chemical digestion

The alimentary canal

The alimentary canal is a muscular tube running from the mouth to the anus. It contracts and relaxes to move food along it – this is **peristalsis**.

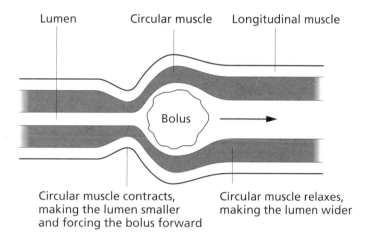

Peristalsis moves the bolus along the alimentary canal.

Sometimes in the course of digestion, the food may need to be kept in the same place (stored) for some time, so there are muscles that can completely close sections of the tube. These muscles are called **sphincters**. The entire tube is **lubricated** with **mucus**.

Lets work along the alimentary canal.

Inside the **mouth** the food is mixed with **saliva**, which is **secreted** from the **salivary glands**. Saliva contains water, mucus and an enzyme called **amylase**. The teeth, lips and tongue grind the food into small pieces. The amylase starts to digest starch, breaking it down into maltose. It does not have time to finish this, though. If you chew a piece of bread for long enough, it will begin to taste sweet.

The mouth makes a ball of food, called a **bolus**, which is swallowed.

The tube in your throat that carries food into the stomach is called the **oesophagus** (sometimes called the **gullet**). It is *behind* the **trachea** (windpipe). On swallowing, a flap called the **epiglottis** covers the trachea to stop food 'going down the wrong way' and ending up in your lungs and choking you.

The food stays in the stomach for between 1 and 2 hours. Here, proteins are broken down to polypeptides. The enzyme at work is called **pepsin**. It requires acidic conditions (pH 2–3). There are various specialised cells in the lining of the stomach which secrete pepsin, mucus and **hydrochloric acid**. The acid kills off any nasty bacteria and neutralises alkali, as well as providing the right pH for pepsin to work. Muscles in the stomach wall contract and relax rhythmically. This helps to break the food down more and mixes it with the **gastric juices** to form **chyme**.

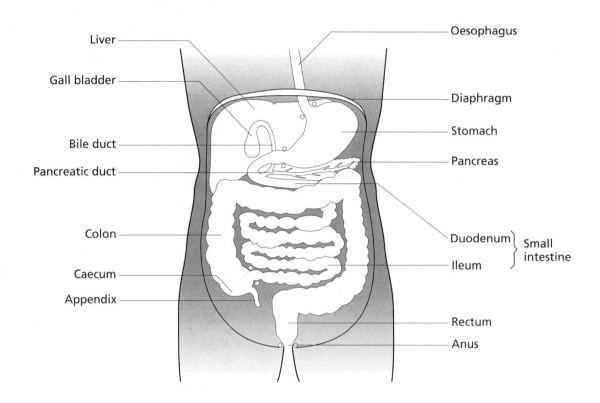

*This diagram shows the abdominal cavity and the key parts of the alimentary canal.
(Pairs of dots ○ ○ show where the sphincters are.)*

Eventually (after about 2 hours), a sphincter at the bottom of the stomach opens up and the chyme flows down to the small intestine. The rest of the chemical digestion takes place in the small intestine.

The small intestine is very long – about 5 metres. This provides plenty of time for digestion and absorption. It has two sections: the first part nearest the stomach is the **duodenum**. This is where food is mixed with **intestinal juice**, **pancreatic juice** and **bile** (more about these in a moment). The lower part, nearest to the **colon,** is called the **ileum**. This is where digested food is absorbed into the blood.

Before going on to describe chemical digestion in all its glory, there's a bit more to say about the structure of the small intestine, which is very specialised.

The wall of the small intestine is covered in finger-like protections called **villi**. Each **villus** is about 1 mm long and is covered with microscopic hair-like structures called **microvilli**.

- The villi and microvilli vastly increase the surface area of the small intestine. This allows rapid absorption of digested food.

- The villi contain blood vessels. Digested food diffuses into the blood and is transported to the liver.

- The **epithelium** of the villi is only one cell thick so digested food can quickly pass into the capillaries.

The digestion process

Back to the top of the small intestine …

The **pancreas** secretes enzymes into the duodenum. The enzymes are contained in the pancreatic juice, which travels into the duodenum via the **pancreatic duct**. Apart from enzymes, the pancreatic juice also contains **sodium hydrogencarbonate** ($NaHCO_3$). This neutralises the hydrochloric acid in the chyme and provides an alkaline pH for the enzymes.

The **liver** produces bile, which is stored in the **gall bladder** behind the liver. Bile travels along the **bile duct** into the duodenum. Bile is a yellowish-green colour. It does not contain any enzymes, but it does contain **bile salts**. These emulsify fats: they turn large droplets into small droplets.

The liver also breaks down old red blood cells, and the broken down pigments are passed into the bile. These pigments have nothing to do with chemical digestion, but they explain why faeces has its characteristic colour.

Some of the enzymes involved in digestion are secreted by cells in the wall of the small intestine. The cells that cover the villi make the enzymes, which stay attached to the surface membranes.

Much of chemical digestion is controlled by enzymes. The table on page 38 shows some information about the enzymes involved in digestion in humans.

All the digestive juices contain water – it helps to split molecules and acts as a solvent. The juices also contain mucus, which acts as a lubricant and is protective.

After digestion, food goes into the **hepatic portal vein** (via the capillaries in the villi) and through to the liver. The food is dissolved in the blood plasma. The liver can break down food further, convert it to something else, store it, or leave it unchanged.

The food that is not digested and absorbed in the small intestine is passed on into the **colon** (not to be confused with a semicolon), also known as the **large intestine**. The colon **reabsorbs water** into the body (living things never waste water), and also reabsorbs salt. If food remains in the colon for too long, too much water is absorbed, causing **constipation**. If food does not stay in for long enough, the opposite occurs: **diarrhoea**.

The **caecum** and **appendix**, which you may have spotted on the diagram, have no obvious function in the human digestive system.

Once water has been reabsorbed, the undigested food is temporarily stored in the **rectum**, prior to **egestion**.

(Remember that this is technically egestion, *rather than excretion; excretion is getting rid of waste products from metabolic reactions, whereas egestion is getting rid of substances that were never used.)*

Part of alimentary canal	Juices secreted	Made by	Enzymes present in juice	Substrate	Products	Other substances present in juice	Function of other substances
Mouth	Saliva	Salivary glands	Amylase	Starch	Maltose		
Stomach	Gastric juice	Gastric pits in wall of stomach	Pepsin (a protease)	Proteins	Polypeptides	Hydrochloric acid	Acidic pH for pepsin; kills bacteria
Duodenum	Pancreatic juice	Pancreas	Amylase	Starch	Maltose	$NaHCO_3$	Neutralises chyme and gives an alkaline pH for the enzymes
			Trypsin (protease)	Proteins and polypeptides	Polypeptides		
			Lipases	Emulsified fats	Fatty acids and glycerol*		
Duodenum	Bile	Liver; stored in gall bladder	None			Bile salts	Emulsify fats
						Bile pigments	Excretory products
Ileum	No juice secreted; enzymes remain on wall of villi	Cells covering villi	Maltase	Maltose	Glucose*		
			Sucrase	Sucrose	Glucose* Fructose*		
			Lactase	Lactose	Glucose* Galactose*		
			Peptidases	Polypeptides	Amino acids*		
			Lipases	Emulsified fats	Fatty acids* Glycerol*		

* These products of digestion are absorbed in the ileum

Worked questions

Q1. *Digestion can be considered as two separate types/processes. What are these two types/processes and where do they take place?*

A1. The two types of digestion are mechanical and chemical.

Mechanical digestion breaks down large pieces of food into smaller ones so that there is a large surface area for chemical digestion. Chewing is part of mechanical digestion. So is the contraction of muscles in the stomach wall.

Chemical digestion is the breakdown of large molecules into smaller ones that can be absorbed. It involves enzymes and happens in the mouth, stomach and most is in the duodenum.

Q2. *Describe how tooth decay comes about.*

A2. Tooth decay results from a build up of plaque which is bacteria and other substances, which then hardens to form tartar. The bacteria in the plaque feed on sugary deposits from foods, producing acid which dissolves the tooth enamel and, if left untreated, right down to the pulp cavity. The bacteria will further infect the gums, leading to gum disease.

Q3. *How does ingested food move down the oesophagus, with no need for lubrication? What is to stop it travelling down the trachea?*

A3. Ingested food moves down the oesophagus by the process of peristalsis, which is repeated contraction and relaxation of the muscle. It is stopped from travelling down the trachea by a flap called the epiglottis, which automatically covers the trachea while you swallow.

Q4. *Describe how the small intestine is so well adapted to its function as the final digestive organ.*

A4. The small intestine is very long so that there is plenty of time for digestion and absorption. The surface of the intestine is covered with villi and microvilli, which are 'finger-like' projections, providing a large surface area for digestion and absorption. The digestive enzymes are on these villi. The villus wall is only one cell thick, and each villus has its own blood supply so that digested materials are absorbed over only a short distance, and are quickly carried away in the blood to the liver.

Q5. *If supplied with a sample of the human enzyme pepsin, at what pH would you expect it to display optimum activity?*

A5. Pepsin digests proteins in the stomach, which has acidic conditions because of the hydrochloric acid that is secreted. Therefore, pepsin must display its optimum rate at acidic pH, probably about pH 2.

topic six
feeding in plants

Photosynthesis

Green plants make their own food; this is called **autotrophic nutrition**. They are able to convert inorganic substances like carbon dioxide and water into carbohydrates.

Green plants make **glucose** from carbon dioxide and water, in a process called **photosynthesis** (so-called because the energy required for the reaction comes from sunlight).

The overall chemical equation for photosynthesis is this:

$$6CO_2 + 6H_2O \xrightarrow[\text{chlorophyll}]{\text{sunlight}} C_6H_{12}O_6 + 6O_2$$

$$\text{Carbon dioxide + water} \xrightarrow[\text{chlorophyll}]{\text{sunlight}} \text{glucose + oxygen}$$

Photosynthesis is actually dead complicated but luckily we're allowed to keep it simple. Photosynthesis can be said to happen in two stages: the **light reaction** and the **dark reaction**.

- In the light reaction, water is split to make hydrogen and oxygen. This stage needs sunlight (hence its name).

- In the dark reaction, the free hydrogen is combined with carbon dioxide to make glucose. This stage doesn't need light. Chemical energy and enzymes are involved in this stage.

So that's the chemistry bit dealt with.

What factors affect the rate of photosynthesis?

- *Light intensity*   We know that sunlight provides the energy for the first stage of photosynthesis. The rate of photosynthesis increases as the light intensity increases – until you reach the maximum rate that the plant can manage.

  Ordinary **white light** (sunlight) is made up of different colour lights of different wavelengths. Chlorophyll *absorbs blue* and *red* light, but *reflects green* light (which is why chlorophyll looks green). If you are growing plants in artificial light (e.g. indoors), you must make sure that they get enough blue and red light. (You can buy special lights.)

  Very bright sunlight can actually damage plants because of the ultraviolet rays.

- *Carbon dioxide*   This is one of the key 'ingredients' for photosynthesis. The more carbon dioxide there is available, the faster the rate of photosynthesis (again, up to a maximum).

- *Temperature* We know from topic three that enzymes usually work faster at higher temperatures, and the enzymes involved in photosynthesis are no exception. Plants will photosynthesise faster on a hot day than a cold one. *But,* if it is too hot, the stomata will close to prevent water loss. This means that photosynthesis will slow down or stop because carbon dioxide cannot diffuse in.

The optimum rate of photosynthesis occurs when temperature, light and carbon dioxide availability are all optimal. If any one of these three factors is reduced, the rate of photosynthesis is reduced. The external factor that restricts the effects of the others is called the **limiting factor**.

Getting a good yield

Farmers and gardeners can make sure they get a good **yield** by making sure that the plants get the best conditions for photosynthesis. One way is to grow plants in a greenhouse. This provides warmth and a fairly constant temperature. Extra light can be provided artificially, and sometimes farmers pump extra carbon dioxide into the greenhouse. It is also important that plants have plenty of water so that they don't wilt.

Yield is also improved by killing pests, removing competition (by killing weeds), and by adding extra nutrients as fertiliser or manure. These things are discussed in topic fourteen.

Finally, it is important that plants aren't planted too close together otherwise they have to compete with each other for their needs, and none of them gets the optimum amount, so none of them grows properly.

What does the plant do with the glucose?

Glucose is used for all sorts of processes in the plant – shown in the diagram. Some of it is used for chemical **respiration** to provide energy for all the other reactions.

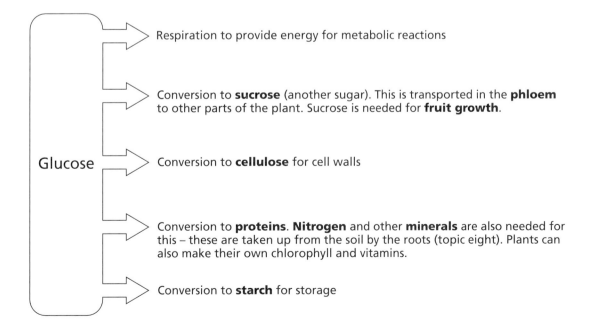

Glucose

Respiration to provide energy for metabolic reactions

Conversion to **sucrose** (another sugar). This is transported in the **phloem** to other parts of the plant. Sucrose is needed for **fruit growth**.

Conversion to **cellulose** for cell walls

Conversion to **proteins**. **Nitrogen** and other **minerals** are also needed for this – these are taken up from the soil by the roots (topic eight). Plants can also make their own chlorophyll and vitamins.

Conversion to **starch** for storage

Plants cannot store glucose as glucose because it is **reactive** and **soluble**. Reactive means that it gets involved in other reactions; soluble means that it has a water potential, affecting the **osmotic balance** of the plant cells.

Glucose is quickly built up into **starch** molecules which are stored in **granules** in the chloroplasts. Starch is unreactive and it is **insoluble** so it does not affect the osmotic balance of the cells.

How to show that plants produce starch
Iodine solution is used to test for the presence of starch. First you need to treat the leaf.

1. Dip the plant in boiling water for about 30 seconds. This destroys the cytoplasm, denatures the enzymes and makes the leaf more permeable to the iodine solution.

2. Put the leaf in a tube of ethanol. Boil the ethanol by placing the tube in a beaker of boiling water. (You cannot use the bunsen burner because ethanol is flammable). The boiling ethanol will dissolve the chlorophyll. (The ethanol will turn green.)

3. Dip the leaf into boiling water again to soften it.

4. Spread the leaf on a flat surface and drip iodine onto it. The parts containing starch will turn blue–black; the parts that do not contain starch will stay yellow or brown (from the iodine solution).

Minerals

As well as the glucose made during respiration, plants need **minerals** to make chlorophyll and proteins such as enzymes. The minerals are obtained from the soil via the root hairs, primarily by **active transport** (topic two). They are transported around the plant in solution in the **xylem** (topic eight).

The minerals needed by plants are summarised below.

Element	Mineral salt	What it is needed for	Deficiency symptoms
Iron	Iron salts	Making chlorophyll (chlorophyll does not actually contain iron)	Young leaves are yellow
Magnesium	Magnesium salts	Making chlorophyll	Yellow between veins of leaves
Nitrogen	Nitrates, or organic compounds containing nitrogen	Making proteins	Poor growth; yellow leaves
Phosphorus	Phosphates	Making ATP (see respiration; topic seven)	Poor growth, especially in the roots

continued:

Element	Mineral salt	What it is needed for	Deficiency symptoms
Potassium	Potassium salts	Keeps a correct balance of salts in the cells	Mottled leaves
Sulphur	Sulphates	Making proteins	Poor growth; yellow leaves

Leaves

Now we know about photosynthesis and what is needed for it, we can go on to leaves and how their structure is adapted (or specialised) for photosynthesis.

We know that photosynthesis uses energy from sunlight. Sunlight is absorbed by the pigment chlorophyll, which is found in **chloroplasts**. (These are organelles.) The chloroplasts also contain the enzymes involved in photosynthesis.

Most of the chloroplasts are in leaf cells, so leaves are adapted to make photosynthesis as efficient as possible.

Structure of the leaf

- The broad part of the leaf is called the **lamina**.

- The stalk is called the **petiole**.

- The veins you can see in a leaf are the **vascular bundles**. In the vascular bundle are the xylem – a tube that transports water and dissolved minerals – and the **phloem** – a tube that carries 'food' (in the form of sugar). (We go on to transport in plants in topic eight, so don't worry about it for now.)

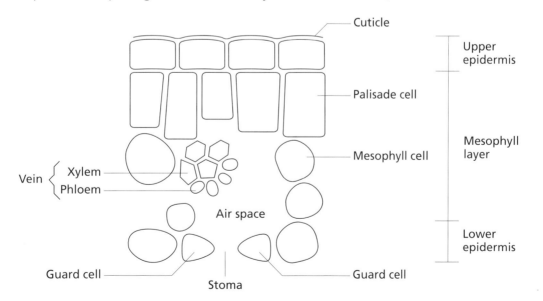

This is a cross-section of a leaf showing the important cell types. Don't forget that the cells are all typical plant cells (see page 6); they all have a cell wall, a nucleus, cytoplasm, mitochondria and a vacuole. The epidermis cells do not contain chloroplasts (except for the guard cells); the cytoplasm of the palisade and mesophylls cells is packed with chloroplasts.

The diagram on the previous page shows a cross-section of a leaf to show the important bits. You can see that it consists of layers of cells.

- The **epidermis** is a bit like the skin of a leaf; it is there for **protection**. It secretes a waxy substance called the **cuticle**, which stops water from evaporating.

  Except for the guard cells, cells in the epidermis don't have any chloroplasts. This means that as much sunlight as possible passes into the **palisade layer**.

- The palisade layer is the top of the **mesophyll** layer (the 'middle' leaf – from 'meso' meaning middle). This layer is *specialised* for photosynthesis. The palisade cells are nearest the top of the leaf where most light gets through. The cells are arranged end-on so that there are as few cell walls as possible between the leaf surface and the chloroplasts. The chloroplasts themselves are cleverly arranged on the broadside of the leaf, so that as much chlorophyll as possible is exposed to sunlight.

- The **spongy mesophyll** is the lower layer of the mesophyll. There are xylem and phloem elements close to each mesophyll cell so that there is a good supply of water, which only has to diffuse a short distance, and products can be taken away quickly.

  The spongy mesophyll contains **air spaces** so gases can diffuse between the palisade cells and the outside air. The gases dissolve into the film of moisture on the cell's surface, and then diffuse into or out of the cell.

- The **stomata** (singular: **stoma**) are pores on the *underside* of the leaf. They allow carbon dioxide to diffuse into the leaf and oxygen to diffuse out of the leaf. The opening and closing of the stomata is controlled by the **guard cells**.

  (Although photosynthesis takes place mainly in the leaves, any part of the plant that contains chlorophyll [i.e. the green parts] can photosynthesise.)

Adaptations of the leaf

From the last section you will have realised (hopefully) that the structure of the leaf is adapted to photosynthesis. There are some adaptations of the leaf as a whole to consider:

- Leaves have a broad flat shape, which provides a *large surface area* for absorption of sunlight and carbon dioxide. This is particularly important when you realise that only *0.03%* of the air in the atmosphere is carbon dioxide!

- The leaves are held out in the air by the petiole and the stem and are arranged so that they overlap each other as little as possible. This allows the maximum possible light to get through.

Worked questions

Q1. *State the equation for photosynthesis.*

A1. The equation for photosynthesis is

$$6CO_2 + 6H_2O \xrightarrow[\text{chlorophyll}]{\text{sunlight}} C_6H_{12}O_6 + 6O_2$$

Q2. *How can the rate of photosynthesis be affected by environmental factors?*

A2. The rate of photosynthesis can be affected by the amount of sunlight. The more sunlight, the greater the rate. It can also be affected by the availability of carbon dioxide, where the more carbon dioxide there is available, the faster the photosynthetic rate. The rate of photosynthesis is also affected by temperature where the greater the temperature, up to a certain point, the faster the rate. However, if it gets too hot, the stomata close to prevent water loss and photosynthesis stops. Each plant has a maximum rate of photosynthesis. The rate can't go above this, even if sunlight, carbon dioxide and temperature continue to increase.

The amount of wind will also affect the rate of photosynthesis: the greater the strength of the wind, the lower the rate of photosynthesis because the stomata will close to prevent excessive water loss.

Q3. *Explain why not all the light reaching the plant is used in photosynthesis.*

A3. Some of the sunlight reaching the plant is the wrong wavelength and therefore cannot be used in photosynthesis. Blue and red light is absorbed by the chlorophyll and used as energy. Green light is reflected and therefore isn't used.

Q4. *Which two features of the leaf prevent water loss?*

A4. The two features of a plant that prevent water loss are firstly the stomata (pores), which are closed by guard cells to prevent loss of water vapour from the leaf, and secondly, the leaves have a waxy cuticle which prevents water loss by transpiration.

Q5. *Give two reasons why the glucose produced during photosynthesis is converted into starch for storage.*

A5. Glucose is reactive, which means that it gets involved in reactions, and soluble, which means that it creates a water potential that would affect the osmotic balance of the plant. Starch is neither reactive nor soluble so is suitable for storage.

Q6. *Explain how a lack of specific minerals leads to inhibited plant growth, using named examples of these minerals.*

A6. Magnesium is an essential component of chlorophyll, which is involved in photosynthesis. Lack of it leads to poor growth and yellowing along the veins of the leaves because of the lack of chlorophyll.

Potassium is responsible for maintaining salt balance in cells. Lack of it causes mottled leaves.

Phosphorus is essential as phosphate in ATP which is vital as an energy supply. Lack of it results in poor growth.

respiration and gaseous exchange

Respiration

Respiration   the process that releases energy from food

Substances from our food are **oxidised** to give carbon dioxide and water, and **energy** is transferred. This is a bit like burning petrol as a fuel to provide energy to run a car.

Glucose is the main substance that is oxidised. The overall equation for respiration is:

$$C_6H_{12}O_6 + 6O_2 \rightarrow 6CO_2 + 6H_2O + energy$$
glucose + oxygen $\rightarrow$ carbon dioxide + water + energy

This reaction doesn't happen all in one go because too much energy would be released too quickly (which is what happens in burning). Instead, it happens in lots of small controlled steps. Each step is catalysed by a particular enzyme.

You can measure the uptake of oxygen by an organism to find out how fast it is respiring – its **metabolic rate**. The apparatus used to do this is called a **respirometer**.

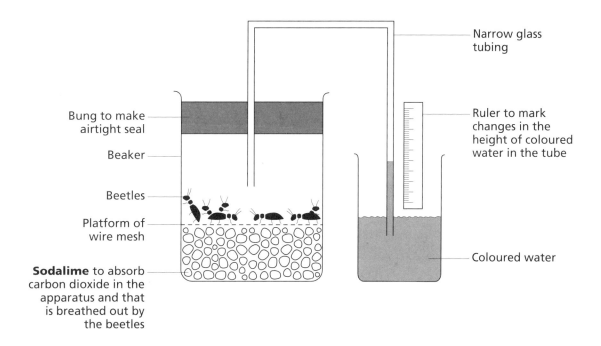

A respirometer is used to measure the uptake of oxygen by beetles. The height of the coloured water will go up at the beginning of the experiment as the carbon dioxide is absorbed. When the water stops moving, start a stopwatch and record the height of the water at timed intervals. This tells you how much oxygen has been used. It is important that you have another respirometer running at the same time that doesn't contain any beetles – this is the **control**. You have to subtract the result of the control from the test respirometer.

The energy released during respiration is not used directly. It is used to drive another chemical reaction: the addition of a **phosphate** group to a molecule called **adenosine diphosphate (ADP)** to form **adenosine triphosphate (ATP)**.

The equation can be written as:

ADP + phosphate + energy → ATP

ATP is made in the mitochondria, which is also where respiration happens. (This is why mitochondria are called the 'power-houses' of the cell.) It acts as a kind of 'energy carrier', taking energy to where it is needed. The energy is released by converting ATP back to ADP:

ATP → ADP + phosphate + energy

Not all the energy from respiration goes into making ATP; some energy is lost as heat. Mammals and birds use this heat to keep warm.

Aerobic and anaerobic respiration

The respiration described above is **aerobic respiration** because oxygen is needed. You can think of it as 'respiration with air'. It is also possible to break down glucose and transfer energy to ATP without oxygen – this is **anaerobic respiration** ('respiration without air').

Anaerobic respiration is less efficient than aerobic respiration, and produces less energy. **Yeast** can respire anaerobically, producing alcohol – the process is called **alcoholic fermentation**. It is used in bread making and to brew beer (see page 166). The process starts once all the oxygen has been used up during aerobic respiration.

The reaction is:

glucose → alcohol + carbon dioxide + energy

Humans can also respire anaerobically for short periods. This can happen during exercise, when breathing and the circulatory system cannot provide enough oxygen for our muscles to keep going aerobically.

Anaerobic respiration is less efficient than aerobic respiration. It produces **lactic acid** which is a mild **toxin** that makes muscles ache.

Oxygen is needed to break down lactic acid to carbon dioxide and water. The amount of oxygen needed to get rid of the lactic acid is called the **oxygen debt**, which must be paid off immediately. This is why your heart rate stays high and it takes a while to get your breath back after you have stopped running – oxygen is still being delivered to the muscles to oxidise the lactic acid. The fitter you are, the quicker you recover.

The equations are:

glucose → lactic acid + energy

lactic acid + oxygen → carbon dioxide + water

Summary of aerobic and anaerobic respiration

Similarities	Differences
• Energy is released by breaking down sugar	• Aerobic respiration produces more energy than anaerobic respiration
• ATP is made	• Aerobic respiration uses oxygen; anaerobic respiration does not
• Some energy is lost as heat	• Carbon dioxide is always produced in aerobic respiration, but not always in anaerobic respiration

Gaseous exchange

Oxygen for respiration has to be obtained from the surroundings. You also have to get rid of the carbon dioxide produced during respiration.

Gaseous exchange   the process of obtaining oxygen and getting rid of carbon dioxide

This gas exchange happens at a **respiratory surface**.

In an *Amoeba*, for example, the cell membrane is the respiratory surface. Oxygen is dissolved in water. Because the *Amoeba* is using up oxygen, the concentration is lower inside than outside the cell, so oxygen diffuses in. Carbon dioxide is being produced during respiration so the concentration is higher on the inside of the cell than the outside. Carbon dioxide therefore diffuses out of the cell.

Surface area and volume

An *Amoeba* is a very small organism and has a large surface area for its volume. This means that the surface is big enough for respiration.

As organisms get bigger, their volume increases by a *cubed* ratio (remember the volume of a sphere is πr^3) but their surface area only increases by a *squared* ratio (e.g. πr^2) (sorry to bring maths into it). This means that the *surface area to volume ratio* gets smaller as the organism gets bigger. Larger organisms cannot exchange gases just through their outer surface because this isn't a large enough respiratory surface for their needs.

Larger animals (like humans) have developed a specialised system for gaseous exchange – the **lungs**.

The tubes going into the lungs – the **bronchi** – branch out into smaller tubes (**bronchioles**), which end in little sacs called **alveoli**. This produces a very big surface area for gaseous exchange.

Features of respiratory surfaces

Respiratory surfaces must:

- have a large surface area for gaseous exchange
- have moist surfaces to stop the cells drying out (the gases dissolve in the liquid before diffusing across the surface)
- be thin so that gases diffuse across quickly
- have a good blood supply so that gases are delivered and carried away quickly.

The respiratory system

The lungs provide the surface for gaseous exchange in mammals.

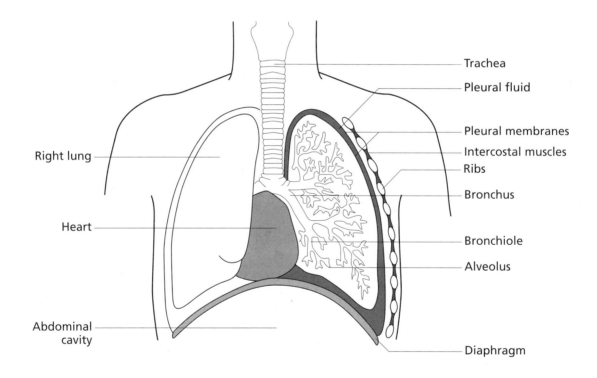

The respiratory tract

The roof of the mouth is called the **palate**; it separates the mouth from the nose so that you can breathe while eating. It is possible to breathe through the mouth (e.g. when you have a blocked nose), although it is generally recommended that one breathes through the nose (but it's a free country so in the end it's up to you). The reason for this is that the air becomes *warm* and *moist* and is *filtered*. Cells on the **turbinal bones** in the nose make a liquid containing water and **mucus**. This evaporates into the air and moistens it. Other cells on the bones have **cilia** (hairs) which beat, wafting the mucus, along with any dust and bacteria trapped in it, to the oesophagus. It is then swallowed. There are cilia all the way down the trachea and bronchi. These do the same job as the cilia in the nose.

The proper name for the **throat** is the **pharynx**. Air passes from the nose, across the pharynx and through a hole called the **glottis**, which leads into the **trachea (windpipe)**. The **epiglottis** is a flap that covers the glottis when you swallow, to stop food going into the trachea (otherwise you choke). This is a **reflex action** that happens when a bolus of food touches the soft palate.

Between the glottis and the trachea is the **larynx (voice box)**. The **vocal cords** vibrate when air passes over them, making sounds.

The trachea is held open by rings of **cartilage**. These rings have gaps on the side nearest to the oesophagus so that the oesophagus can expand when food is swallowed.

In the **thorax (chest)** the trachea divides into two tubes called bronchi (singular: **bronchus**). One bronchus goes to each lung.

Inside each lung, the bronchus splits into smaller bronchioles; it branches out. At the end of the bronchioles are the alveoli, which are groups of small **air sacs**. The **alveolar wall** is the respiratory surface of humans. The total area of the respiratory surface is about 100 m^2.

The walls of the alveoli are only one cell thick so the gases don't have to diffuse far. The alveoli have **capillaries** wrapped around them; this provides the blood supply.

There are thousands of capillaries to all parts of the lung, providing the transport system needed for gaseous exchange.

The diagram shows what happens in the alveoli.

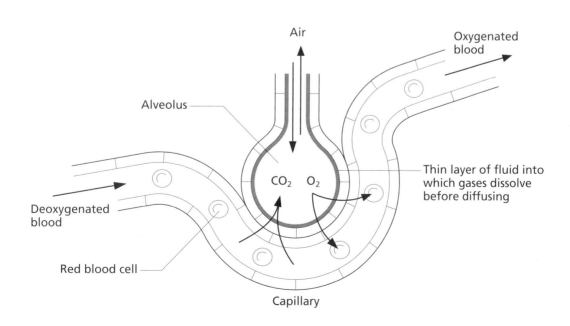

Gaseous exchange between an alveolus and a capillary

The **pleural membranes** surround each lung. They help the lung **adhere** to the **ribs** and also prevent it rubbing against the ribs. The pleural membranes make **pleural fluid** which provides **lubrication** so that the membranes can move over each other as you breathe.

The pleural membranes are separate for each lung. Each **pleural cavity** is airtight so that if one lung stops working, the other one can carry on working.

(The lungs are light and spongy because of the numerous spaces [alveoli]; butchers sometimes refer to sheep's lungs as 'lights'.)

Breathing

For gaseous exchange to happen, air must be sucked into the lungs (**inspiration**) and pushed out again (**expiration**).

Two sets of muscles are involved in breathing. The **intercostal muscles** move the ribs up and down. The ribs are held in place by the **sternum**. The **diaphragm** is a sheet of muscle and elastic tissue between the chest and the abdomen.

Inspiration

The diaphragm **contracts** and moves downwards. This *increases* the volume in the thorax. At the same time, the **external intercostal muscles** contract, making the ribs move *up* and *out*. (Remember the song: moving on up, moving on out, nothing can stop me …) This also increases the volume of the thorax.

Because the volume of the thorax increases, the pressure decreases (Boyle's law don't you know). The pressure outside the thorax is greater than inside, so air goes into the lungs to equalise the pressure – inspiration.

*(**Inspiration** and **inhalation** both mean breathing in.)*

Expiration

The diaphragm relaxes, moving upwards. The external intercostal muscles move the ribs downwards and inwards. These two movements decrease the volume of the thorax, pushing the air out because of the increased pressure.

When you breathe out forcefully, such as when you are coughing, the **internal intercostal muscles** and the muscles in the wall of the abdomen contract forcefully, pushing more air out.

*(**Expiration** and **exhalation** both mean breathing out.)*

The following table shows you the composition of inspired and expired air.

	Inspired air	Expired air	Reason for difference
Oxygen	21%	16%	Oxygen is absorbed, and used in respiration
Carbon dioxide	0.03%	4%	It is a waste product produced during respiration and is expired
Water content	Variable	High	The respiratory surface is kept moist, and the moisture may evaporate and be lost in expiration
Temperature	Variable	Higher than air (usually)	Air is warmed when passing through the respiratory passages
Argon and other inert gases	1%	1%	Not used by cells
Nitrogen	78%	78%	Not used by cells

Breathing rate

We breathe without having to think about it. (We can think about it, but we don't *need* to.) A special group of cells in the base of the brain controls breathing.

If we need more oxygen, or have too much carbon dioxide (or lactic acid) in our blood, the brain makes us breathe faster and deeper. This is what happens during exercise, when our muscles produce more carbon dioxide and need more oxygen. Our heart rate also increases so that the gases are transported to and from the muscles quickly.

Smoking

You must have heard adults going on about smoking being bad for you. Here's why.

Cigarettes contain **nicotine** and **tar**, and cigarette smoke contains **carbon monoxide**.

Nicotine is a **stimulant** (it makes you feel good) but it is also a *poison*. (If all the nicotine from one cigarette was extracted and injected into you in one go it would kill you!) Nicotine diffuses into the blood stream. It increases blood pressure and the amount of fatty substances in the blood. This leads to **heart disease**. Nicotine is **addictive** which means that it is hard to give up.

Tar contains lots of chemicals called **carcinogens** – these are substances that cause **cancer**. Tar is absorbed by cells lining the bronchi and bronchioles. These cells may start dividing, forming a thicker layer than normal. If the cells go on dividing, cancer can develop.

Tiny particles in smoke *irritate* the lining of the trachea and bronchi. The cilia are damaged and extra mucus is produced. Instead of being wafted to the throat by the cilia, the mucus collects in the lungs, which makes you cough. If the tubes get infected, you get **bronchitis**, which can be **chronic** – it doesn't get better.

Lots of coughing eventually damages the alveoli so there is less surface for gaseous exchange. This makes the person short of breath. This illness is called **emphysema**.

Carbon monoxide in smoke attaches *irreversibly* to haemoglobin in the blood. Haemoglobin is the pigment that usually carries oxygen. Obviously if it is carrying carbon monoxide it carries *less* oxygen. Carbon monoxide is very difficult to remove from haemoglobin so this effect lasts a long time. In a heavy smoker, as much as a *fifth* of the haemoglobin is wasted because it is combined with carbon monoxide.

Carbon monoxide also affects the growth of babies in the womb. Women who smoke tend to have smaller babies than non-smokers. They are also more likely to have a miscarriage.

Respiration and gaseous exchange in plants

Plants get their energy in the same way as animals: through respiration. They do not need as much energy as animals because they don't move, but they do need it for growth, reproduction, active transport and certain reactions (like building starch from glucose).

Just a reminder: during the day plants are photosynthesising so they are *using carbon dioxide* and *producing oxygen*. They are also respiring, which *uses oxygen* and *produces carbon dioxide*. The *net* movement of gases therefore depends on the balance of respiration and photosynthesis.

- On a bright day, photosynthesis will be faster than respiration, so the net movement of gases will be: carbon dioxide in, oxygen out.

- At night there is no photosynthesis, only respiration, so the net movement is: oxygen in, carbon dioxide out.

Hydrogencarbonate indicator can be used to detect the presence of carbon dioxide – its colour changes from *red* to *yellow* in the presence of carbon dioxide.

If you put a plant in a sealed flask that also contains hydrogencarbonate indicator, in the dark the indicator will go yellow. This is because the plant is only respiring so it is giving off carbon dioxide. If you move the flask so that it is in bright light, the indicator will slowly turn back to red. This is because the plant is photosynthesising and respiring, so it will be using more carbon dioxide than it is producing. The indicator changes colour as the carbon dioxide is used up.

You can also use lime water in this experiment, which turns cloudy when carbon dioxide is bubbled through it.

The structure of leaves means that plants have a high surface area to volume ratio. Diffusion into the leaves is sufficient to provide the plant with gases for respiration and photosynthesis. Go back to topic six to remind yourself how plants' leaves are adapted for gaseous exchange.

Gaseous exchange in fish

Fish absorb oxygen dissolved in water through **gills**. Herring have four gills. Each one is made up of a curved **gill bar** which has stiff **gill rakers** projecting from one side (these filter food from the water, which is then swallowed) and leaf-like tissue called **gill lamellae** projecting from the other side. The gill lamellae are the respiratory surface and are especially adapted for this: they are very thin, very branched so that they have a large surface area, and have a good blood supply. The blood in the capillaries flows in the opposite direction to the flow of water – **a counter current** – which improves gaseous exchange. The gaps between the gills are called **gill pouches**. These are open to the outside; the opening is covered by the **operculum**, a flap made of skin and bone.

A fish takes in water through its mouth and forces it between the gills and out through the gap covered by the operculum. Gaseous exchange happens as the water passes over the gills. Some fish make breathing movements: as they open their mouth, the floor of the pharynx is pulled down. This increases the space inside it so that water flows into the mouth and pharynx. To breathe out, the floor of the pharynx is pulled up, squeezing the water out. By coordinating the movements of the mouth and operculum, there is a continuous flow of water over the gills. This flow is called the **respiratory current**.

Gaseous exchange in worms

Worms are fairly inactive so they don't need a lot of oxygen. They can absorb what they need through the skin. The skin is thin and moist and has a network of capillaries to deliver and collect gases. Loops of capillaries project up into the epidermal layer so that the distance for gas exchange is very short. The thin moist skin means that the worm is very prone to water loss through evaporation so it has to stay inside its burrow for most of the time.

Frogs can also exchange gases through the skin. They also have lungs for obtaining extra oxygen when they are out of the water. They are restricted to staying in damp areas to stop the moist skin from drying out.

Worked questions

Q1. Write down the equation for aerobic respiration.

A1. Aerobic respiration:

$$C_6H_{12}O_6 + 6O_2 \rightarrow 6CO_2 + 6H_2O + energy.$$

Q2. In humans, if anaerobic respiration occurs, what product is produced. What are the two main disadvantages of anaerobic respiration occurring in man? What product is formed if yeast respires anaerobically, which makes them ideal for the fermentation process?

A2. Lactic acid is produced if anaerobic respiration occurs in humans. The main disadvantages of anaerobic respiration occurring in humans are that it produces little energy, it produces a toxic substance and as a result, an oxygen debt forms, which has to be paid back later when aerobic respiration resumes.

Alcohol is produced when anaerobic respiration occurs in yeast, which makes them ideal for the fermentation process.

Q3.   *How are the respiratory surfaces so well adapted to their function?*

A3.   The respiratory surfaces are involved in gaseous exchange. They are adapted so that diffusion is as rapid as possible. This is achieved by having a large surface area and only a short distance over which diffusion has to occur (the surfaces are only one cell thick). The surface is moist so that gases can dissolve into and out of the air into the water for diffusion. Respiratory surfaces also have a rich blood supply so that diffused gases are transported to and from them quickly.

Q4.   *Why is it generally healthier to breathe through your nose rather than through your mouth?*

A4.   When you breathe through your nose, the air is filtered. Cilia and mucus trap particles and bacteria so that they don't enter the lungs. This means that there is less chance of infection if you breathe through your nose. Also, air is warmed and moistened as it passes through your nose. Breathing in cold air through your mouth can irritate the trachea and bronchi.

Q5.   *Premature babies often require surfactant to be injected into their lungs in order to moisten them, in order to help them breathe. Explain how moistening the interior of the lungs aids breathing?*

A5.   Moistening the surface of the lungs improves gaseous exchange. The gases dissolve into and out of the moisture for diffusion.

Q6.   *Explain the mechanism of inspiration and expiration in terms of the pressure changes in the lungs and the contraction and relaxation of muscles.*

A6.   During inspiration the diaphragm contracts and moves downwards. The external intercostal muscles contract, pulling the rib cage upwards and outwards. These movements increase the volume of the chest, which means that the pressure inside the chest is lower than outside the chest so air enters the lungs.

During expiration, the external intercostal muscles relax and the ribs move downwards and inwards. The diaphragm relaxes, moving upwards and becomes domed. Air is forced out of the lungs as the volume of the chest decreases and the pressure increases.

Q7.   *This is a diagram of the human chest; label the diaphragm, the trachea and the pleural membranes.*

A7.

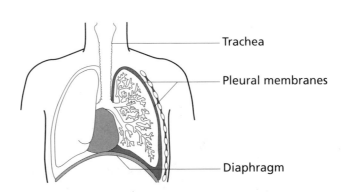

Q8. *Smoking is now recognised as a very unhealthy habit. Explain in terms of tar, nicotine and carbon monoxide, how these aspects make smoking unhealthy?*

A8. Tar is an irritant and makes cells in the surface of the lungs inflamed (bronchitis) and they produce more mucus. This accumulates, preventing the cilia from working and trapping bacteria. Extra mucus also makes you cough a lot to get rid of it, which eventually damages the lungs (emphysema). Tar also contains carcinogens which can cause cancer. The irritant effect of tar also makes the lining cells divide a lot, which can lead to cancer.

Nicotine is very addictive, which makes smoking become a habit. Nicotine also increases blood pressure and can cause heart disease.

Carbon monoxide combines more readily with haemoglobin than oxygen does, to form carboxyhaemoglobin, which is difficult to break apart. This reduces the oxygen-carrying capacity of the blood.

Q9. *What does the plant use the energy produced from respiration for? Is the rate of photosynthesis higher than the rate of respiration?*

A9. In plants, the energy produced from respiration is used for growth, active transport, reproduction and the production of starch from glucose.

The rate of photosynthesis is higher than the rate of respiration during daylight. There is no photosynthesis when it is dark, so that only respiration is occurring. Overall, the two processes balance out.

transport systems

Large organisms need transport systems to carry useful substances to where they need to be, and to carry waste away.

The circulatory system

Oxygen and other substances are transported round the body by the **circulatory system**. This consists of the **heart**, a network of **blood vessels** (**arteries**, **veins** and **capillaries**), and the **blood**.

Blood that contains oxygen is called **oxygenated** blood. The oxygen is combined with the pigment **haemoglobin** in red blood cells, forming **oxyhaemoglobin.** Blood whose oxygen has been used up is called **deoxygenated** blood. (This may seem pretty obvious but it's worth having a reminder before going on to the next bit.)

The heart

The heart is made of **cardiac muscle**.

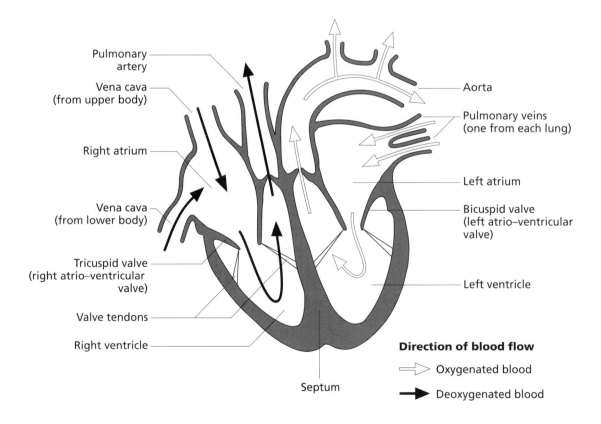

The important parts of the human heart

The heart has four **chambers**: the left and right **atria** (singular: **atrium**) and the left and right **ventricles**. Blood comes into the heart via the atria and is pumped out from the ventricles. The two sides of the heart are separated by the **septum**.

The atria pump blood into the ventricles, which is a very short distance, so they don't need to be very muscular. The ventricles pump blood out of the heart. The walls of the ventricles are therefore thicker and more muscular than the walls of the atria.

The left ventricle pumps blood out to the whole body whereas the right ventricle only pumps blood to the lungs. The wall of the left ventricle is therefore much thicker and more muscular (i.e. stronger) than the wall of the right ventricle.

The heart pumps blood around the body by continuously contracting and relaxing.

During **diastole** the heart is *relaxed* so it becomes bigger. The atria fill with blood.

During **systole**, the heart *contracts*. It becomes smaller and the blood is squeezed out. Systole happens in two stages. First, the muscles of the atria contract, forcing the blood into the ventricles. Secondly, the ventricles contract, forcing blood out into the arteries.

There are valves called **atrio–ventricular valves** between the atria and ventricles. These make sure that blood doesn't go back into the atria when the ventricles contract. The valve on the *left* side of the heart is called the **bicuspid valve** – it has two parts; the valve on the *right* side of the heart is called the **tricuspid** valve – it has (you've guessed it) three parts. When the ventricles contract, the pressure forces the valves upwards so they are closed. **Tendons** tighten and stop the valves going back too far (or turning inside out).

The heart rate

We already know that the heart beats (contracts and relaxes) regularly. When resting, your heart beats about 72 times every minute (which is pretty regular really) – the **heart rate** is 72 beats per minute (bpm). The range is 50–100 bpm. During exercise, when your muscles need more oxygen, this rate can go up to 200 bpm.

So, what controls your heart rate? The heart beat is initiated by the **pacemaker** – a small group of specialised muscle cells at the top of the *right atrium*. These cells send electrical signals to the rest of the heart muscle so that all the muscle contracts together at the right time.

The pacemaker has two sets of nerves going to it from the brain. One tells the heart to beat faster, the other tells it to slow down. This means that the heart can meet the needs of the body.

> *(Something rather weird about the heart is that it would carry on beating on its own if you took it out of the body [at least for a while]. This means that the mechanism that makes it beat is in the heart itself. [If you want to show off you can say that the heart has its **own inherent rhythm** – as long as you explain what that means!]*
>
> *Another amazing thing about cardiac muscle is that it can keep on contracting without getting tired.)*

Artificial pacemakers are small electronic devices that can be used to control the heart rate if the natural pacemaker cells stop working properly. The electronic device is implanted in the abdomen and wires are connected to the ventricles. Regular pulses of electricity tell the ventricles when to contract – usually about once every second. Artificial pacemakers can last for several years.

Blood supply to the heart

In order to keep contracting regularly, the heart needs a good supply of oxygen. This is provided by the **coronary arteries** which branch out over the heart. (These arteries are the first to get blood from the aorta, so the blood is very freshly oxygenated.)

Heart attack

If one of the coronary arteries gets blocked, the cardiac muscle doesn't get enough oxygen and stops contracting. This is called a **cardiac arrest** or **heart attack.**

The inside of the coronary arteries can become lined with a fat-like substance called **cholesterol** – this process is called **athersclerosis** (hardening of the arteries). This makes the arteries narrower, with less room for the blood to get through. It also means that an artery can be blocked by a blood clot, which is what happens in a heart attack.

Atherosclerosis is caused by eating saturated rather than unsaturated fat, and by smoking. (Go back to pages 25 and 53 if you've forgotten about these.)

The double circulation

Humans have a **double circulation** system. This means that blood goes through the heart *twice* in each circuit of the body. This will become more obvious as we work our way round the circulatory system. (Use the diagram opposite to follow the route.)

- Freshly *oxygenated* blood from the lungs enters the *left atrium* via the **pulmonary vein**.
- The blood flows from the left atrium into the *left ventricle*.
- The blood is pumped from the left ventricle into the **aorta** – the main artery of the body.
- The oxygenated blood goes via arteries to all the organs in the body, where the oxygen is used.
- *Deoxygenated* blood from the organs returns towards the heart in veins. The largest veins are the **vena cavae** (singular: **vena cava**); there are two of these: one from the head and one from the lower body.
- Deoxygenated blood from the vena cavae goes into the *right atrium*.
- From the right atrium the blood flows into the *right ventricle*.
- The blood is then pumped to the lungs via the **pulmonary artery**.
- The blood is oxygenated in the lungs, and we are back at the beginning.

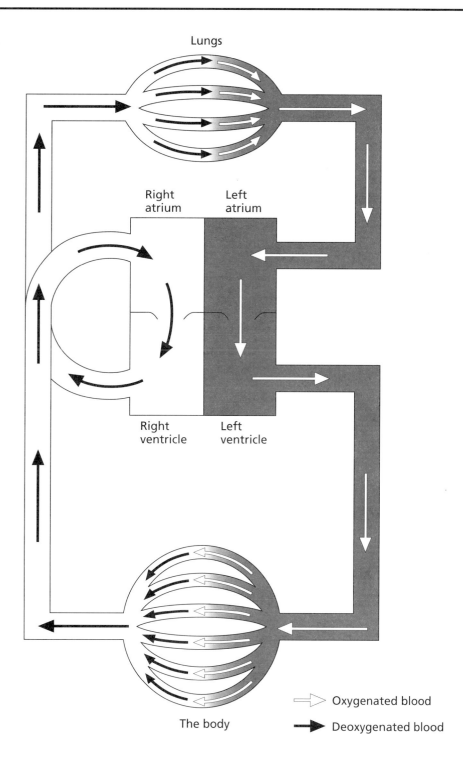

Lungs

Right atrium

Left atrium

Right ventricle

Left ventricle

The body

⇨ Oxygenated blood

➡ Deoxygenated blood

A rather diagrammatic representation of the double circulation system in humans

Blood vessels

So far, we have talked gratuitously about different blood vessels without actually explaining what they are. So this is what I shall do now. (It's always hard to know what to talk about first.)

Blood vessels are tube-like structures that transport blood around the body. There are three main types: arteries, capillaries and veins.

Arteries

Arteries carry blood *away from the heart*. This blood is under high pressure because of the powerful contractions of the ventricles. To cope with this the arteries have *thick elastic* walls. (This is yet another example of adaptation or specialisation.) The blood moves along the arteries as the heart beats. The elastic wall of the artery stretches and recoils with each **pulse** to keep the blood flow smooth. You can feel this stretching and recoiling in the pulse in your wrist. (This flow can be described as **pulsatile**.)

The aorta is the main artery in the human body and carries blood at the highest pressure. Arteries to each organ branch off the aorta. These arteries branch further to make **arterioles**.

Nearly all arteries carry *oxygenated* blood. Exceptions are the pulmonary artery which carries deoxygenated blood to the lungs (this is still *away* from the heart) and the *umbilical artery*, which takes deoxygenated blood away from the fetus.

Capillaries

Blood vessels branch even more from the arterioles into the capillaries. Capillaries are very small diameter tubes – just big enough for red blood cells to squeeze through. All the tissues in the body have a capillary **network** and every cell is within easy reach of a capillary (i.e. close enough so that molecules can diffuse quickly backwards and forwards). To make diffusion even easier, capillary walls are only one cell thick. Oxygen and food are provided to cells and waste products are taken away. Blood therefore becomes deoxygenated as it passes through the capillaries. Capillaries join up to form veins.

Veins

As well as becoming deoxygenated while passing through the capillaries, the blood loses most of its pressure. The flow of blood is *slow* and *smooth* rather than pulsatile. Because of this, the walls of the veins don't need to be thick and strong. Instead the walls are thin. The **lumen** (the space inside the vessel) is bigger than in arteries; this lets the blood flow along easily.

The blood is squeezed along the veins by the contraction of muscles – like moving your legs. (Veins don't have their own muscles, but there are other muscles around them.) This pushes blood back to the heart (against gravity).

Veins have **valves** in the walls to stop blood going backwards – these are a bit like 'watch pockets'.

Veins carry blood *back to the heart*. This is usually *deoxygenated* blood. Exceptions are the pulmonary vein, which carries oxygenated blood back to the heart from the lungs, and the umbilical vein, which carries oxygenated blood to the foetus.

The main veins in the body are the **anterior vena cava**, which brings blood back from the upper body, and the **posterior vena cava**, which brings blood back from the lower body. (Anterior and posterior mean front and back, respectively.)

Sometimes as people get older the blood flow in the veins gets sluggish. The walls of the veins can become stretched and a bit flabby – these are **varicose veins**.

If a person lies in bed for a long time, the leg muscles are not pushing the blood along the veins. The blood might flow so slowly that a **clot** forms. A blood clot is called a **thrombosis**. This is dangerous because if the clot gets to the lungs, it could get stuck in the arterioles. This is called a **pulmonary embolism** and can stop part of the circulation, which could kill you.

Summary of arteries and veins

Arteries	Veins
• High pressure	• Low pressure
• Thick elastic walls	• Thin walls, large lumen
• Pulsatile flow	• Smooth flow
• No valves	• Valves to prevent backflow
• Carry blood *from* the heart	• Carry blood *to* the heart
• Carry oxygenated blood*	• Carry deoxygenated blood*

*Except the pulmonary and umbilical veins and arteries

Blood supply to the organs

Each organ has its own blood supply: an artery and a vein.

Liver: **hepatic** artery and vein, and the **hepatic portal vein** which brings blood from the intestines to the liver; this blood contains absorbed food

Alimentary canal: **mesenteric** artery and vein

Kidney: **renal** artery and vein

Arm: **subclavian** artery and vein

Leg: **femoral** artery and vein

Head: **carotid** artery (you can feel the pulse in your neck) and **jugular** vein

Blood

That's all the structural bits. Now let's get onto the liquid bit.

Blood is the **transport medium** in the circulatory system of humans (and lots of other mammals for that matter).

The liquid part of the blood is **plasma**. The rest of the blood is:

• **red blood cells (erythrocytes)**, which carry oxygen

• **white blood cells**, which are involved in the **immune response**

• **platelets**, which are fragments of cells involved in **blood clotting**.

Plasma

Plasma contains the following things.

- *Water*   It is absorbed in the colon, transported to all cells in the plasma, and excess is removed by the kidneys. Water acts as a **solvent** for the other substances in the plasma (which are called **solutes**). Plasma is 90% water.

- *Fibrinogen, antibodies* and other *proteins*   Fibrinogen is made in the liver, and helps in the clotting of blood. Antibodies are made by lymphocytes (one of the types of white blood cell), providing protection against foreign cells like bacteria. Antibodies and fibrinogen remain in the blood in case they are needed.

- *Fatty acids and cholesterol*   These have been absorbed in the ileum, or are from the fat reserves in the body. They are being transported either to the liver (to be broken down for energy) or to the adipose tissue (fat) to be stored.

- *Glucose*   This has either been absorbed in the ileum or has been produced by the breakdown of glycogen in the liver. It is being transported to all cells for respiration. Glucose could also be on the way *to* the liver or muscles to be converted to glycogen for storage.

- *Urea and other waste (excretory) products*   Urea is produced in the liver from the breakdown of excess amino acids (**deamination**). (Hopefully you remember that amino acids come from the breakdown of proteins; they cannot be stored.) The waste products go to the kidneys to be excreted.

- *Mineral ions* e.g. sodium (Na^+) and chloride (Cl^-)   Ions are absorbed in the ileum and colon. They are taken to all cells; the excess is excreted by the kidneys.

- *Hormones*   These are secreted by **endocrine glands** and are carried to all parts of the body; each hormone only affects its **target organ** (see topic ten).

- *Dissolved gases*   Carbon dioxide is released by all cells as a waste product of respiration. Most of it is *dissolved* in the plasma as **hydrogencarbonate ions** (HCO_3^-). It is carried to the lungs to be excreted. (Oxygen for respiration is carried to cells by the red blood cells.)

Red blood cells

- Red blood cells are also called erythrocytes.
- They are **biconcave** discs (doughnut-shaped). This shape means that they have a large surface area to volume ratio for gas exchange.
- They do not have a nucleus. The lack of a nucleus makes room for even more haemoglobin.
- They are produced in the **bone marrow** (that's the spongy bit inside bones) of some bones (vertebrae, ribs, some limb bones) at an awesome rate: about 9000 million (9 000 000 000 – it looks even more awesome with all the zeros) every hour.

- Red blood cells do not live long – only about 4 months. (This is because they don't have a nucleus. This short lifespan also explains why the bone marrow is kept so busy making new ones.)

- Old red blood cells are broken down in the liver, **spleen** and bone marrow. The iron in haemoglobin can be used again so it is stored for making new haemoglobin. Excess iron is made into **bile pigments** which are released in bile into the duodenum and are excreted in the faeces.

- A quick recap of haemoglobin: this is the protein in the cytoplasm of red blood cells. It is dark purplish-red. It combines with oxygen to make oxyhaemoglobin (which is bright red); oxyhaemoglobin easily breaks down to oxygen and haemoglobin where the oxygen is needed. The different colours of haemoglobin and oxyhaemoglobin explain why deoxygenated and oxygenated blood look different.

White blood cells

There are two main groups of white blood cells: **phagocytes** and **lymphocytes**. Phagocytes and B lymphocytes are produced by the bone marrow. T lymphocytes are made in the **thymus**.

Phagocytes

Phagocytes prowl around in the blood looking for pathogens (bacteria and viruses) and dead body cells, which they destroy by phagocytosis – they engulf their prey and digest it. Phagocytes can change their shape. They can squeeze through gaps in capillary walls and reach almost any part of the body. Phagocytes are summoned to a graze or cut to destroy any pathogens that might try to get in.

Lymphocytes

B lymphocytes are found in the **lymph nodes**. They destroy germs by releasing **antibodies**. Antibodies are specific for particular **antigens** – proteins on the surface of cells. Antibodies destroy cells bearing antigens by making them clump together, or by 'labelling' them for phagocytosis by phagocytes. Antibodies that neutralise toxins are called **antitoxins**.

Only B lymphocytes secrete antibodies. The other type – T lymphocytes – deal with cells that are infected with viruses by 'wearing' the antibodies on their surface. There are several types of T lymphocyte. **Killer cells** attack and destroy cells infected with viruses. They also attack transplanted organs unless immunosuppressive drugs are given to the patient to stop this happening. **Helper cells** help B lymphocytes and phagocytes to do their jobs. **Suppressor cells** act as brakes to stop the system going out of control.

When a lymphocyte recognises its particular antigen, it replicates itself rapidly (by mitosis), producing lots of identical cells (**clones**) which then deal with the pathogen.

The first time your immune system encounters an antigen, it takes a few days to produce lymphocytes and appropriate antibodies. Some of the lymphocytes stay in the lymph glands as **memory cells**. If they encounter their antigen again, they mount a response very quickly, killing the pathogen before it can breed. This is the basis of **immunity.**

Platelets

These are small fragments of cells, and do not contain a nucleus. They are made in the bone marrow. Platelets are involved in blood clotting.

> *(If you damage your skin, a blood clot forms to stop pathogens getting into the body, and to stop you losing too much blood. When blood vessels are damaged, platelets stick onto the damaged edges. The platelets and the damaged tissue around the wound release chemicals that make other things happen:*
>
> - *A long chain of reactions that converts **prothrombin** in the plasma to **thrombin** is set off.*
>
> - *Thrombin is an enzyme. It changes **fibrinogen** in the plasma into **fibrin**.*
>
> *Fibrin is an insoluble protein. It forms fibres which make a mesh across the wound. Platelets and red blood cells get trapped in the mesh, forming a blood clot.)*

The functions of blood

The blood has three main functions.

Transport
You will already have realised that blood carries all sorts of things around the body, from where they are produced, to where they are needed or stored. Waste materials and excess things that cannot be stored are also transported by the blood to the organs that will excrete them (mostly liver, kidneys and lungs).

Defence against disease
The white blood cells produce antibodies and engulf invading organisms. Blood clotting is also part of this defence.

Temperature regulation
Parts of the body that have a high respiration rate produce a lot of heat: the liver, muscles and **brown fat**. This heat warms the blood, which then carries the heat elsewhere in the body. In this way, the liver etc. don't overheat, and other parts of the body are kept warm.

The capillaries in the skin help to keep the body temperature *constant* at 36.8°C. When you are too hot the capillaries **dilate** (they get wider) so that more blood goes to the surface of the skin and heat is lost by radiation to the air. (This is why you go red when you exercise.) When you are too cold the capillaries **constrict** (get narrower) so that blood doesn't go to the surface and the heat is kept inside the body. (This is why you are pale in cold weather.) Keeping a constant body temperature is part of **homeostasis** which we get onto in topic eleven.

Lymph and tissue fluid

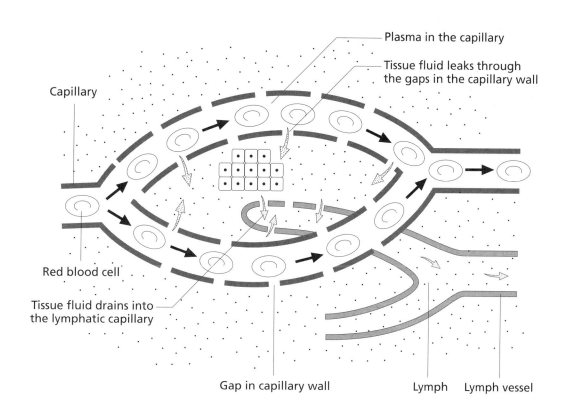

Plasma in the capillary

Tissue fluid leaks through the gaps in the capillary wall

Capillary

Red blood cell

Tissue fluid drains into the lymphatic capillary

Gap in capillary wall

Lymph

Lymph vessel

Formation of tissue fluid and lymph

Tissue fluid immediately surrounds cells. It supplies cells with all their nutrients, including oxygen. The nutrients diffuse from the blood, into tissue fluid and into the cells. Waste products diffuse in the opposite direction. The tissue fluid environment is kept constant by homeostasis.

Tissue fluid is actually plasma and white blood cells that have leaked out of the capillaries. There are **gaps** between the cells in capillary walls that allow this to happen. Red blood cells can't get through the gaps because they are too big and can't change their shape. White blood cells squeeze through the gaps by changing shape.

Tissue fluid *continually* leaks out of the capillaries and returns to the blood via the **lymph system**. It drains into **lymphatic capillaries**, which join up to form **lymph vessels**. These carry the **lymph** (drained tissue fluid) to the **subclavian veins**, where it rejoins the blood. (The subclavian veins bring blood from the arms back to the heart.)

On its way from the lymph vessels to the subclavian veins, the lymph passes through various **lymph nodes**. These contain vast numbers of white blood cells, which destroy bacteria and toxins in the lymph.

Lymph flows more slowly than blood because the lymphatic system doesn't have a pump to move it along. Lymph vessels have valves (like the veins), which stop the lymph flowing backwards.

Transport in flowering plants

Plants are less active than animals so their cells don't need materials so quickly. Also, the shape and structure of plants means that oxygen and carbon dioxide can *diffuse* into and out of cells.

Plants have two transport systems:

- The **xylem** carries water and dissolved minerals.

- The **phloem** carries the 'food' materials that the plant has made. (You can remember which is which because phloem and food start with the same sound.)

Xylem and phloem tubes are found together in a group called a **vascular bundle**.

The xylem

Xylem vessels run from the roots, up through the stem and out into each leaf. The xylem is made of *hollow dead* cells joined end to end. The cells don't contain any cytoplasm or nuclei. The cell walls are made of cellulose and **lignin**, which is very strong and helps keep the plant upright. The ends of the cells have disappeared so that a long continuous tube is formed.

A new xylem is formed each year, and the old xylem is pushed to the centre and becomes compacted. The xylem at this point is almost entirely lignin – this is wood.

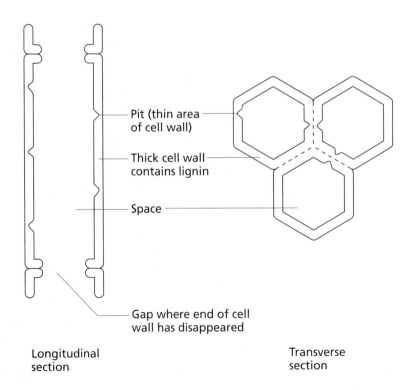

Pit (thin area of cell wall)

Thick cell wall contains lignin

Space

Gap where end of cell wall has disappeared

Longitudinal section

Transverse section

Structure of the xylem

The phloem

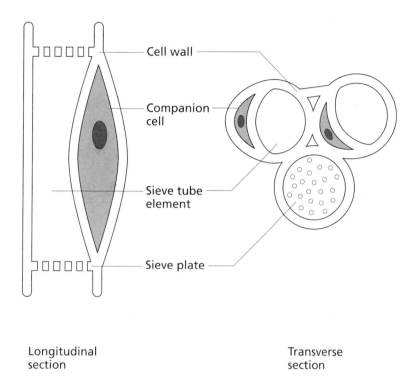

| Longitudinal section | Transverse section |

Structure of the phloem

The phloem is also made up of cells joined end to end. The ends of the cells are not completely broken down and form a kind of sieve (logically called a **sieve plate**). Each of the cells is called a **sieve tube element**. These cells contain strands of cytoplasm, but no nucleus, and there is no lignin in the cell wall (but there is cellulose of course).

Each sieve tube element has a **companion cell** attached to it. The companion cells have a nucleus, organelles and dense cytoplasm, and provide the sieve tube elements with some of their requirements.

Transport of water

Water enters the plant through **root hairs** on the **root tip**. Each root hair is a long **epidermal** cell. These cells are short-lived and are replaced frequently.

The very end of the root tip is called the **root cap**. This is a layer of cells that protects the root as it grows. The rest of the root is covered by a layer of cells – the **epidermis**. The root hairs start above the root cap.

Water is absorbed into the root hair by **osmosis**. The cytoplasm and cell sap in the root hairs has a high concentration of solutes, which means a low concentration of water. The concentration of water (or **water potential**) is higher outside the root tip than inside it, so the water diffuses into the cell. (Don't forget that plant cells have a partially permeable membrane across which osmosis occurs.)

The water travels by osmosis from cell to cell and into the xylem in the centre of the root.

Water is literally sucked up the xylem, just like you suck cola up a straw. This happens because there is a **pressure gradient**: the pressure at the top of the xylem is lower than at the bottom, so the water moves upwards. (Capillary action aids this only to a small degree.)

The pressure at the top of the xylem system is kept low because of **transpiration**. This is the **evaporation** of water from the plant's leaves. The cells inside the leaf are each covered in a film of moisture. Some of this moisture evaporates from the cells and diffuses out through the **stomata** – pores on the underside of the leaf.

The moisture that evaporates is replaced by water from the xylem by osmosis. This reduces the effective pressure at the top of the plant, so water is drawn upwards. This process is known as the **transpiration stream**.

Conditions that affect the rate of transpiration

Temperature   As temperature increases, there is more energy available for evaporation, so transpiration increases.

Humidity   This is the amount of moisture in the air. As humidity increases, there is more water in the air. This reduces the difference in water concentration between the inside and outside of the leaf, so diffusion is slower. So, the higher the humidity, the slower the transpiration rate.

Wind speed   Water evaporates quickly on a windy day because the diffused molecules are taken away by the wind. So, transpiration increases in windy weather.

Light intensity   Light provides energy for evaporation. Also, on bright days, plants photosynthesise very quickly. The stomata open to allow carbon dioxide to diffuse in; this also allows water to diffuse out.

Water supply   Plants close their stomata when water is in short supply. This will decrease the rate of transpiration.

Adaptations to prevent water loss

Transpiration is useful because it keeps water moving up through the plant. However, it is important that the plant doesn't lose more water than the root can take up; if this happens the plant **wilts**.

Plants have *adaptations* that help prevent water loss.

*(Very dry conditions are called **xerophytic** conditions.)*

Closure of stomata   When the stomata are short of water, the guard cells become **flaccid** and the stomata close. When there is plenty of water, the guard cells become **turgid** (full of water) and the stomata open. The structure of the guard cells allows this to happen: the inner wall is thick and cannot stretch as much as the thinner outer wall, so when the guard cells absorb water, the cells curve, forming the opening.

Plants need the stomata to be open so that carbon dioxide can diffuse in for photosynthesis. The stomata only close at night, and on hot, dry days, when the plant can't photosynthesise.

Waxy cuticle   This is made by the cells in the epidermis and keeps the leaf waterproof. Holly leaves have a thick waxy cuticle.

Hairy leaves   Some plants have hairy leaves to prevent water loss. The hairs trap a layer of moisture next to the leaf. This reduces the concentration gradient between the inside and outside of the leaf, so evaporation is slowed down.

Stomata on the underside of the leaf   Most plants have more stomata on the underside of the leaf than the upper surface. Less light reaches this surface so it is cooler and transpiration is slower here than on the upper surface. Some stomata may be in pits.

Decreasing the surface area   Plants that live in very hot conditions often have spines rather than leaves. These have a much smaller surface area than leaves, so there is less area for evaporation. Although this helps to conserve water, it also means that photosynthesis is slow.

Uptake of mineral salts

Root cells take up ions dissolved in the soil water by **active transport** (see page 14). This is because the minerals are in a higher concentration inside the root hair than in the soil, so the minerals have to be taken up against the concentration gradient. Special **carrier proteins** in the cell membrane of the root hair take up the minerals; the energy is supplied by the mitochondria.

Transport of organic food

Carbohydrates made in the leaves during photosynthesis are used by the plant to make proteins, oils and other organic substances. Organic food material, particularly sugar, is transported in the phloem tubes to where it is needed. This is called **translocation**. The sap inside phloem tubes contains lots of sugar. Moving it is an *active* process that uses energy.

Worked questions

Q1.   *After oxygenation by the lungs, describe the motion of the blood via the heart, to the rest of the body, back to the heart until the blood returns to the lungs for reoxygenation.*

A1.   After oxygenation by the lungs, the blood is carried via the pulmonary vein to the left atrium which then opens into the left ventricle. From the left ventricle, the blood is pumped via the aorta and other arteries around the body.

The blood becomes deoxygenated as it passes around the body. It returns via the veins and vena cavae to the right atrium of the heart, which then opens into the right ventricle. From here, the blood is pumped back to the lungs via the pulmonary artery for reoxygenation.

Q2. *An excess intake of cholesterol is known to lead to heart disease. Explain how this occurs.*

A2. Excess cholesterol causes a build up of fatty deposits in the coronary arteries, which supply the heart with oxygen and nutrients. These deposits cause narrowing of the arteries, which therefore means that the heart muscle gets insufficient oxygen and nutrients. If the arteries get completely blocked, no oxygen gets to some muscle, which causes a heart attack.

Q3. *Explain why a pacemaker may need to be fitted to a person with an irregular heartbeat.*

A3. The heart needs to beat regularly to keep blood pumping round the body, supplying all the tissues with oxygen and nutrients. An artificial pacemaker sends regular electrical impulses to the heart muscles to make them contract, keeping the heartbeat regular.

Q4. *Compare the three types of blood vessel, relating their structure to their function.*

A4. The three types of blood vessel are arteries, veins and capillaries. Arteries have thick elasticated walls, to withstand the high pressure of the blood due to the pumping action of the ventricles. Veins have thinner walls because the blood is no longer at high pressure. Valves in the veins prevent the back-flow of blood, which is travelling against gravity (back up) to the heart. Capillaries have very thin walls, so that nutrients and oxygen can diffuse out quickly and waste products can diffuse in quickly.

Q5. *One of the functions of the blood is a transport medium. Name the four most important substances carried by the blood. Name the other two main functions of the blood.*

A5. The four most important substances carried by the blood are gases (oxygen and carbon dioxide), hormones, minerals and waste products.

The other two main functions of the blood are as a defence against disease, because it carries/transports the white blood cells and antibodies, and as a temperature regulation mechanism.

Q6. *Carbon monoxide poisoning is a great risk in houses with poorly serviced central heating boilers and gas fires. Explain how the carbon monoxide can ultimately lead to death.*

A6. Haemoglobin combines much more readily with carbon monoxide than oxygen. Carboxyhaemoglobin is formed, and does not readily release the haemoglobin. This means that the oxygen-carrying capacity of the blood is reduced. Eventually this inhibits respiration and can lead to death.

Q7. *Explain why a lymph system is necessary.*

A7. Plasma leaks out of capillaries to form tissue fluid around individual cells. This tissue fluid drains into the lymph system, which returns the lymph to the blood in the vena cavae.

Q8. *Explain the function of the xylem and phloem and why they are essential to the plant.*

A8. The xylem of a plant carries water through the plant up from the roots. It gives the plant support as well as transporting water around the plant. The phloem carries food through the plant.

Q9. *The process whereby water is lost from a plant is known as transpiration. Explain how this process can be increased. Explain how excess water loss / transpiration is prevented.*

A9. The rate of transpiration is increased by:

a) increasing temperature because the water molecules have more energy and diffuse more quickly

b) sunlight because the molecules have more energy

c) wind because molecules are borne away, maintaining the gradient for diffusion

d) decreased humidity because the air is less moist so there is more of a gradient for diffusion.

Excessive transpiration is prevented by closing the stomata, pores on the underside of the leaf. Some plants are adapted to minimise water loss by transpiration.

a) Hairy leaves trap a layer of moisture against the leaf, decreasing the gradient for diffusion.

b) The stomata may be buried in pits so that a layer of moisture is trapped, again decreasing the concentration gradient for diffusion.

c) The waxy cuticle on leaves prevents water loss.

d) Some plants, like cacti, have spines, decreasing the surface area over which transpiration can occur.

the continuity of life

Cell division

Chromosomes

All cells contain **chromosomes**, which are strands of **DNA** embedded in a protein structure. The chromosomes contain **genes**; each gene is a small section of the DNA strand. The chromosomes exist in pairs. These pairs are called **homologous chromosomes**. The corresponding genes on each chromosome have the same function. A human cell contains 46 chromosomes; 23 pairs. Different animals have different numbers of chromosomes.

Each chromosome has a **centromere**, a point of attachment during cell division. During cell division, each chromosome replicates to form two identical **chromatids**.

Growth and **reproduction** in organisms occur by **cell division**. There are two types of cell division – **mitosis** and **meiosis**.

Mitosis

Mitosis   two **daughter** (new) **cells** are produced from one parent cell; both daughter cells are **genetically identical** to the parent cell

Growth occurs by mitosis. For example, a human being starts off life as a single cell. This cell grows and divides into two cells, then each one grows and divides again, forming four cells, and so on.

Many organisms use mitosis in order to reproduce, such as *Amoeba*. This is **asexual reproduction** and produces genetically identical offspring. Mitosis is the only type of cell division used in organisms that undergo asexual reproduction. Only one parent is needed for reproduction.

The next bit describes the mechanism of mitosis. (You don't need to know it in such detail, but I think it helps to explain it.)

Interphase: The cell is metabolically active but is not dividing; the chromosomes are so long and thin that they are invisible. The DNA replicates during late interphase.

Prophase: The chromosomes become short and fat, and can be seen using a light microscope. Each chromosome has replicated to form two chromatids. A **spindle** composed of fibres develops across the cell from the **centrioles**.

Metaphase: The nuclear membrane vanishes. The chromosomes line up along the equators of the spindles.

Anaphase: The centromeres divide, and the chromatids separate from each other. They are pulled away from each other by the spindle fibres.

Telophase: The chromosomes are at opposite ends of the cell, and form into groups. The spindle fibres disappear, and a nuclear membrane forms around each set of chromosomes.

Late telophase: The cytoplasm divides, forming two daughter cells. The chromosomes become invisible again, as the cell goes into interphase.

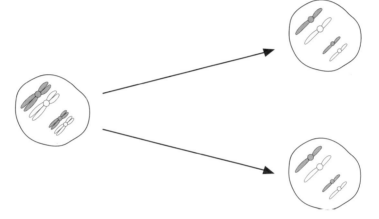

The parent cell contains four chromosomes

Each chromosome splits and one chromatid from each chromosome goes into each daughter cell

Two identical daughter cells

Summary of mitosis

Sexual reproduction and meiosis

Sexual reproduction requires *two* parents. Each parent produces sex cells called **gametes**. A normal cell has two versions of each chromosome, and is called a **diploid** cell. A gamete cell contains only *one member of each homologous pair* of chromosomes, and is called a **haploid** cell.

In sexual reproduction, the two gametes fuse together, forming a new cell, which is called the **zygote**. This fusion is called **fertilisation**. The zygote is a diploid cell. For example, in humans, each gamete has 23 chromosomes. The zygote then has 46 chromosomes.

Gametes are produced by meiosis, which always involves a *halving* of the chromosome number.

Early prophase I: The chromosomes become short and fat and therefore visible, having already replicated into two chromatids. The chromatids remained attached at the centromere.

Late prophase I: The homologous chromosomes, each made up of two chromatids, come together, to form **bivalents**.

Metaphase I: The bivalents line up on the spindle fibres at the equator.

Anaphase I: The centromeres do not split. The bivalents separate and the homologous chromosomes are pulled away from each other along the spindle fibres. (The two chromatids of each chromosome are still joined together.)

Telophase I: The chromosomes arrive at opposite ends of the cell; nuclear membranes appear around each group. The spindle fibres disappear, and both the cytoplasm and the centrioles divide.

Prophase II: New spindles are formed at right angles to the first ones.

Metaphase II: The chromosomes line up on the equators of the spindles.

Anaphase II: The centromeres split; the chromatids separate, and move away from each other, along the spindle fibres.

Telophase II: The chromatids arrive at opposite ends of the cell. Nuclear membranes form around them and the cytoplasm divides. Four new daughter cells have been formed.

Meiosis forms *four* daughter cells (gametes), each of which is haploid. Meiosis only occurs in the production of gametes.

During *late prophase I* in meiosis chromatids of homologous chromosomes may swap pieces between themselves by breaking and re-forming. This is called **crossing over**. These pieces carry genes. This means that each of the four gametes produced has a *different combination* of genes, and that this combination is different from the parent cell. So, whereas mitosis produces daughter cells that are identical to each other and to the parent cell, meiosis produces daughter cells that are different. This produces **variation** among the offspring.

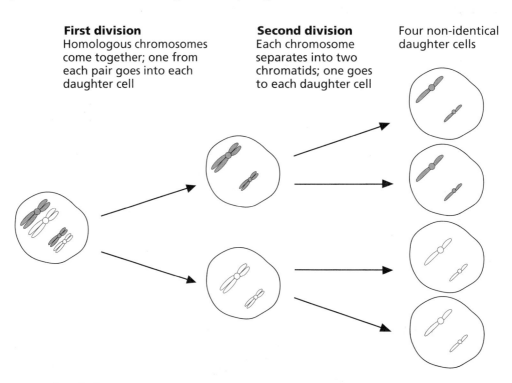

First division
Homologous chromosomes come together; one from each pair goes into each daughter cell

Second division
Each chromosome separates into two chromatids; one goes to each daughter cell

Four non-identical daughter cells

Summary of meiosis

Gametes

The female gamete is large and does not move much: this is the **egg** (or **ovum**; plural: **ova**) in humans. The male gamete is much smaller and can move, actively searching out the female gamete. This is the **sperm** (or **spermatozoa**) in humans.

Organisms usually only produce one type of gamete. For example, all mammals are either male or female, producing sperm or eggs, respectively. However, some organisms produce both types of gametes. These are **hermaphrodites**. Most flowering plants are hermaphrodites, the flower bearing both **pollen grains** (male gametes) and **ovules** (female gametes). Earthworms are also hermaphrodites.

Sexual reproduction in humans

The female reproductive organs

The female gametes (ova) develop in the **ovaries**. An ovum, once mature, moves into the funnel-shaped opening of the **Fallopian tube** (or **oviduct**), which leads into the **uterus**. The uterus has thick muscular walls. It is quite small – about the size of a fist – but it stretches during pregnancy. The neck of the uterus has a narrow opening called the **cervix**. This leads to the **vagina**, which is open to the outside.

The eggs form in the ovaries before a girl is born. The eggs are made from cells in the **epithelium** (outside layer) of the ovary. Some of these cells move towards the centre of the ovary and a small space filled with fluid forms around each one. Each space and the cell inside it is called a **follicle**. There are thousands of these follicles in the ovaries at birth.

The follicles begin to develop at **puberty**. Usually only one develops every month. The cell and the fluid-filled space around it grow bigger and the follicle moves to the edge of the ovary. It is now called a **Graafian follicle**. During this process the developing egg has been undergoing *meiosis* – only one of the daughter cells becomes an egg.

At **ovulation** the Graafian follicle bursts and the egg is pushed out into the funnel of the oviduct. The funnel is lined with beating **cilia**, which waft the egg along the oviduct. **Peristalsis** also helps. Eventually, the egg reaches the uterus. The empty Graafian follicle shrivels and develops into the **corpus luteum** (yellow body).

What happens next depends on whether or not the egg was fertilised by a sperm in the oviduct. (We'll get on to this once we've done the male reproductive organs.)

The menstrual cycle

Usually, one egg is released from the ovary each month. While the follicle is maturing, the lining of the uterus becomes thick and spongy. It is full of tiny blood vessels, ready to supply an **implanted embryo** with food and oxygen.

If the egg is not fertilised within 3 days of ovulation it dies. It doesn't implant into the uterus but continues downwards and out of the vagina. The spongy lining of the uterus is not needed, and this disintegrates and is shed through the vagina. This is **menstruation** or a **period**. This happens on days 1–6 of the menstrual cycle. Ovulation usually happens on day 14. The whole menstrual cycle takes about 28 days.

Hormones and the menstrual cycle
The menstrual cycle is controlled by the following hormones:

- **follicle stimulating hormone** (FSH)
- **luteinising hormone** (LH)
- **oestrogen**
- **progesterone**.

The **pituitary gland** is the 'master gland' in the brain. It secretes FSH which causes the follicle to develop. The developing follicle secretes oestrogen, which stimulates the development of the uterus lining. A peak in the level of oestrogen causes the secretion of LH from the pituitary. This stimulates ovulation.

At ovulation, the Graafian follicle becomes the corpus luteum. The follicle no longer secretes oestrogen. The corpus luteum secretes progesterone which maintains the lining of the uterus, preventing menstruation. It also inhibits the production of FSH so that no more eggs ripen in the ovaries (at least for the time being).

If the egg is fertilised, the corpus luteum continues to secrete progesterone, and the woman misses her period. The **placenta** takes over secretion of progesterone during pregnancy, maintaining the lining of the uterus and preventing menstruation, which would lead to a **miscarriage**.

If the egg is not fertilised, the corpus luteum disappears after a few days. Progesterone is no longer produced and, because the uterus lining is no longer maintained, menstruation occurs. FSH is secreted again, so another follicle starts to ripen. Oestrogen is secreted so the uterus lining starts to build up again.

The male reproductive organs

The male gametes (spermatozoa or sperm) are produced in the **testes**. These are in the **scrotal sac (scrotum)** which hangs outside the body. The sperm are stored in the **epididymis**. They travel along a tube called the **vas deferens** (plural: **vasa deferentia**) which joins with the **urethra**, just below the bladder. The urethra carries sperm and urine, but not at the same time. The sperm swim in a fluid called **semen**. The fluids in the semen are produced in the **prostate gland** and the **seminal vesicles**. The urethra leads to the outside via the **penis**.

The testes (singular: **testis**) contain thousands of narrow coiled tubes called **tubules**. This is where sperm are made. The cells in the wall of the tubules divide by *meiosis* to form the sperm. Sperm are made continually, from puberty onwards.

Production of sperm is very sensitive to heat. Sperm will not develop if the temperature is too high. This is why the testes are outside the body in the scrotum where it is slightly cooler than inside the body.

Fertilisation

We left the egg being wafted along the Fallopian tube. If the egg is not fertilised by a sperm 8–24 hours after it is released, it dies. This means that the sperm must reach the egg while it is near the top of the Fallopian tube if fertilisation is to happen.

When the man is sexually excited, blood is pumped into spaces in the **erectile** tissue and the penis becomes **erect**. The penis is pushed inside the woman's vagina. Muscles inside the walls of the vasa deferentia contract rhythmically. The wave of contraction sweeps from the testes, along the vasa deferentia and into the penis. The sperm are squeezed along, mixed with semen, and out of the urethra. This is called **ejaculation**.

The sperm are deposited in the vagina, near to the cervix. They are still quite a long way from the egg. Using their tails, they swim up through the cervix and uterus to the Fallopian tube.

Sperm can only swim at about 4 mm per minute, so it takes quite a long time to reach the oviduct. Many of them never make it that far. About one million sperm are deposited in the vagina during ejaculation, so there is a good chance that some are strong enough to reach the egg.

The successful sperm 'eats' into the jelly that surrounds the membrane of the egg using special enzymes contained in a vesicle in the sperm's head. As soon as the egg membrane is penetrated by one sperm, it changes and becomes impenetrable, keeping other sperm out. The unsuccessful sperm die.

The head of the sperm that penetrates the egg separates from the tail, which stays outside the egg.

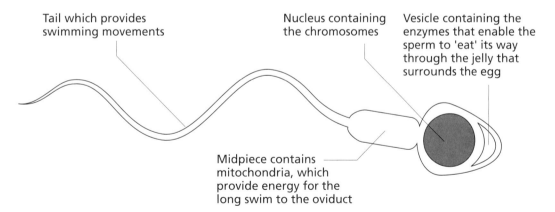

The structure of a sperm cell is very specialised. The sperm is about 0.05 mm long.

The egg and sperm nuclei fuse, forming a zygote. The zygote moves along the Fallopian tube and at the same time the cells start to grow and divide by *mitosis*. After a few hours it has formed a ball of cells called the embryo. By the time the embryo reaches the uterus it has 16 or 32 cells. The cells obtain food from the **yolk** of the egg.

Development of the fetus

The uterus has a spongy lining, and the embryo sinks into it. This is **implantation**. As the embryo grows, the placenta also grows. This has projections called **villi** that fit closely into the uterus wall. The placenta is the life-support system for the embryo, which is joined to it by the **umbilical cord**. This contains the **umbilical artery** and the **umbilical vein**. The artery takes blood away from the embryo to the placenta, and contains deoxygenated blood. The vein brings oxygenated blood to the embryo from the placenta. The placenta has capillaries containing blood from the embryo. The wall of the uterus has spaces containing the mother's blood. The bloods do not mix but are separated by the thin wall of the placenta. Oxygen and food diffuse across the placenta into the umbilical vein, and travel to the embryo. Carbon dioxide and other waste products diffuse across the placenta into the mother's blood. The placenta grows as the embryo develops.

The embryo is held in a 'bubble' called an **amnion**. It is a strong membrane, containing a fluid called **amniotic fluid**. The amnion supports and protects the embryo, acting as a shock absorber. During pregnancy, the cervix is plugged with mucus.

During **gestation** (development of the embryo) the embryo grows, and by 11 weeks it has all its vital organs, and is called a **fetus**. The development process is complete after about 9 months (the gestation period).

Birth

By the time it is ready to be born, the fetus is usually lying head downwards, with its head lying just over the opening of the cervix.

Birth starts when the muscles of the uterus start to contract. This is **labour**. The contractions gradually become stronger and closer together and after a few hours the cervix is stretched wide enough open.

The muscles then start to push the baby down through the cervix and out through the vagina. The contractions also cause the amnion to burst. When it is born, the baby is still attached to the uterus by the umbilical cord and placenta. The placenta comes away from the uterus and is pushed out. This is the **afterbirth**.

The umbilical cord is clamped and cut. This is painless because there are no nerves in the cord. The end of the cord shrivels up and forms the baby's **navel** (belly button).

Twins

If the zygote divides in two on its way to the uterus, two identical sets of cells become embedded in the wall of the uterus. Two genetically identical twins will be born.

If two different eggs are fertilised by two sperm, two zygotes are embedded in the wall of the uterus. Two non-identical twins will be born. It is possible for non-identical twins to be a boy and a girl, or the same sex. Identical twins are always the same sex (obviously, otherwise they wouldn't be identical).

Contraception

Contraception is the prevention of fertilisation when **sexual intercourse** takes place. **Barrier methods** work by putting a barrier between the egg and the sperm. **Condoms**

and the **cap** are examples. The **oral contraceptive pill** uses hormones to prevent ovulation. The ovaries are kept in the state they would be in if the woman were pregnant, and no eggs are released.

Condoms   The condom is a rubber sheath placed over the erect penis. It traps semen, preventing it entering the vagina. Condoms are reliable if used correctly. They can also prevent the transfer of **HIV** (see page 160) and **sexually transmitted diseases** between partners.

Cap (diaphragm)   This is a circular rubber sheet which is placed over the cervix. **Spermicidal** (sperm killing) cream is applied to the edges first. Sperm cannot get past the cap to the uterus. This is a very effective method if used correctly. The first fitting is done by a doctor, but after that the woman can position the cap herself.

The oral contraceptive pill   One pill is taken every day. The hormones in the pill stop eggs from being released. This is an effective method as long as the woman takes the pill each day. The pill can cause unpleasant side-effects, and the woman must visit her doctor regularly.

Intrauterine device (IUD)   A device is placed inside the uterus. (This is done by a doctor.) This doesn't prevent fertilisation, but prevents any embryo that forms from implanting into the uterus.

Sterilisation   The vasa deferentia are cut in the man, stopping sperm from travelling from the testes to the penis. The oviducts are cut or tied in the woman, stopping eggs from travelling down the oviduct. These are *permanent* because once tubes are cut or tied, they cannot be reopened.

Rhythm method   The woman keeps a record of her menstrual cycle and avoids sexual intercourse for a few days around the time when ovulation is predicted to occur. It is difficult to know exactly when ovulation occurs so this isn't a very safe method. Ovulation can be detected by a slight rise in body temperature.

Using hormones to improve fertility

As well as being used in the contraceptive pill to prevent ovulation, hormones can also be used to *stimulate* the production of eggs in the treatment of **infertility**. FSH and LH are used to do this. If the woman's Fallopian tubes are blocked, the woman is given enough hormone so that several eggs ripen. The eggs are removed from the ovary and combined with her husband's sperm in a petri dish. Fertilised eggs are then put into her uterus where hopefully they will grow into an embryo. Although this sounds easy, it is quite a tricky business and doesn't always work.

Sexual reproduction in flowering plants

Plants can reproduce asexually – by **vegetative propagation** – or sexually, which is where **flowers** are involved.

Most flowering plants are hermaphrodite. (Just in case you've forgotten, this means that they have both male and female gametes.) Some plants are **unisex**, for example the holly.

Structure of a flower

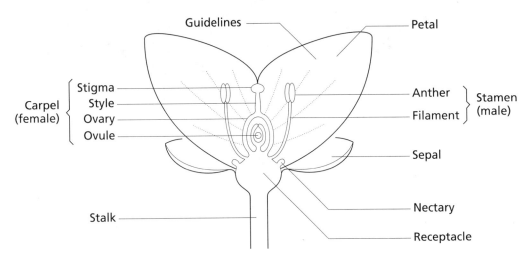

The important parts of a flowering plant

The **petals** are the most obvious parts of a flower. They are brightly coloured to attract insects. On the petals are **guide-lines** running from the top to bottom; these guide the insect to the base of the petal to the **nectary** gland. The nectary makes **nectar**, a sugary liquid that the insects feed on. While the flower is still a bud, the petals are protected by the **sepals**, which can be the same colour as the flower, or green.

The female parts

The female part of a flower is the **carpel** in the centre. It consists mostly of the ovary, which contains the ovules; these contain the female gametes. Meiosis takes place in the ovules, forming the egg cells. Each ovule contains one egg cell. The top of the carpel is the **stigma** held up by the **style**. The stigma catches pollen.

The male parts

The **stamens** are the male parts of a flower. The **filament** of the stamen holds the **anther** at the top. The anthers produce pollen, a yellowy powder that contains the male gametes. The anther contains four spaces called **pollen sacs**. Cells around the edge of the pollen sac divide by meiosis to make pollen grains. When the flower bud opens, the anthers split open so that the pollen is on the outside of the anther.

Pollen grains from different types of flower are different shapes.

Pollination

Pollination is the transmission of pollen (which contains the male gametes) to the stigma (which is close to the female gametes).

Some plants, particularly flowers, are pollinated by insects. The insect is attracted to the plant by its brightly coloured petals and perfume. It is guided to the nectary by the guide-lines, brushing past the anthers on the way. Pollen will stick to the body of the insect and when the insect visits the next flower, some of this pollen will brush off onto the stigma. (The stigma is sticky to help this happen).

Some plants are pollinated by wind. These plants don't usually have petals (or have small inconspicuous petals), scent or nectaries. The anthers dangle outside the flower to catch the wind. The stigma is usually large and feathery and also dangles outside the flower to catch passing pollen. Pollen is small and light so that it can be easily blown by the wind, and is made in very large amounts because a lot of it is lost.

Self-pollination is when pollen is carried to the stigma of the *same* flower, or to another flower of the same plant.

Cross-pollination is when the pollen is carried to a flower on a different plant of the same species. Pollen usually dies if it lands on a different species of plant.

Fertilisation

For fertilisation to occur, the male gametes in the pollen have to reach the female gamete in the ovule.

If pollen lands on the right kind of stigma it starts to grow a **pollen tube** (a long tube) which digests its way through the style using enzymes. The ovule is surrounded by a double layer of cells called the **integuments**. At one end is a small hole called the **micropyle** through which the pollen tube grows.

Once the pollen tube is in the ovule, the male gamete travels along the tube to the female gamete. Fertilisation is the fusion of the two gametes.

One ovule is fertilised by one pollen grain. If there are several ovules in the ovary, then each will need a pollen grain to be fertilised.

Seeds

A fertilised ovule becomes a **seed**. The zygote starts to grow inside the ovule to form the **embryo**. The embryo has a **radicle** which will grow into a root, and a **plumule** which will grow into a shoot. There is also food for the embryo stored in the **cotyledons** (or seed leaves) as starch and protein. (The cotyledons are the white fleshy parts of runner bean seeds.) The cotyledons also contain enzymes.

The integuments, which were wrapped around the ovule, harden and become the **testa**, which is the protective coating of the embryo. The testa and embryo form the seed. The testa stops the embryo being damaged and prevents bacteria and fungi from entering.

The testa bears a scar, called the **hilum**, where it has broken off from the pod or fruit. It also has a pore that allows water to enter during **germination**. The pore is the micropyle.

If the seed contains hardly any water, it stays **dormant**. There is no metabolism, and it will survive harsh conditions like drought. If certain conditions are fulfilled (see below), the seed will start to germinate.

Fruit

The ovary grows into a fruit to protect the seeds until they are ripe and to help **disperse** them.

The dispersal of seeds is important to decrease competition between plants. If plants are too crowded, they have to compete for water, light and nutrients and may not grow properly. Dispersal also allows plants to **colonise** new areas.

Seeds can be dispersed in different ways.

- In the wall flower, the fruit is hard and dry. When the seeds are ripe, the fruit splits open and the seeds are carried away by the wind.

- In broom plants the **pericarp** (the wall of the fruit) dries and suddenly twists. This opens the fruit and throws the seeds out. This is **self dispersal**.

- Some seeds, such as the sycamore, are adopted for **wind dispersal**: the pericarp forms wings around the seeds.

- Other seeds have hooks on the pericarp so that they stick to animals' fur and are dispersed.

- Some fruits are eaten by birds or animals and the seeds are excreted – this is also dispersal.

> *(In biology, the word fruit has a very precise meaning: it is an ovary after fertilisation, containing seeds. Tomatoes and bean pods are fruits, as well as the more obvious ones like apples, plums and blackberries.*
>
> *Fruits contain one or more seeds, and have two scars – one where it was attached to the plant, and one where the stigma and style were attached. Seeds have only one scar [the hilum] where it was joined to the fruit.)*

Germination

The seed will start to germinate when certain conditions are fulfilled.

- *Water* is present to hydrate the protoplasm, and allow metabolism.

- There is *warmth* for enzymes to work.

- There is *oxygen* for respiration.

- Some seeds may need *light*, but many do not; first they need to be able to respire, and use the food stored in the cotyledons. Before this store has run out, they start to **photosynthesise**.

When the seed begins to germinate, it takes up water through the micropyle. The cotyledons swell and the testa bursts. The enzymes start to work: **amylase** breaks down stored starch to form maltose, and **proteases** break down the proteins to form amino acids.

Maltose and amino acids dissolve in the water and are used by the embryo plant for growth. Amino acids are used to make new proteins for the cytoplasm and cell membrane. The maltose is converted to glucose. Some of this is used to make cellulose for cell walls but a lot of it is used for respiration, providing energy for growth.

When the seed first germinates, its weight increases because it absorbs water from the soil. As it uses up its food store, the seed loses weight.

After a few days, the plumule appears above ground and the first leaves can photosynthesise. The plant can now grow quickly because it is making its own food. The first leaves are actually the cotyledons, which turn green and start to photosynthesise. The plumule then opens out and grows into a shoot.

Sexual versus asexual reproduction

Hopefully you remember that asexual reproduction involves mitosis, and produces genetically identical offspring. Sexual reproduction involves meiosis and fertilisation. During fertilisation, genes from two different parents are joined in a new combination, and the offspring are different to the parents. Sexual reproduction therefore produces variation.

If a plant is growing well in one place and has plenty of room, it may reproduce asexually; this produces lots of offspring quickly. These plants are identical to the parent and so are well **adapted** to the conditions. The disadvantage is that, because the plants are all identical, they are all vulnerable to the same diseases and the whole population could be lost in one go.

If a plant is having difficulty surviving or if it is crowded, sexual reproduction is more advantageous than asexual reproduction. The seeds are dispersed to new areas. Because the offspring are different to the parents, there is a good chance that some of them will be adapted to their new conditions and will thrive.

Summary

- Asexual reproduction is useful in *unchanging* conditions. The offspring will already be adapted to living in their environment.

- Sexual reproduction is useful in an *unstable* environment. The offspring are different to the parent and may be able to survive in new conditions. This is important for *colonisation* of new areas, and for **evolution**. (More about evolution in topic sixteen.)

Worked questions

*Q1.   A human egg cell contains 23 chromosomes.
How many chromosomes does a human zygote contain?*

A1.   46

*Q2.   Name the types of cell division occurring in the production of the egg cell and
in the development of the zygote.*

A2.   Meiosis occurs in the production of the egg cell; mitosis occurs in the
development of the zygote.

*Q3.   Describe the similarities and differences between these two types of cell
division [meiosis and mitosis].*

A3.   Both mitosis and meiosis produce new daughter cells; two are produced in
mitosis, whereas four are produced in meiosis.

In both mitosis and meiosis, the chromosomes (i.e. the DNA) replicate before
cell division. In meiosis there are two stages of division: first the homologous
chromosomes separate, then the chromatids separate. In mitosis there is only
one stage of division in which the chromatids separate.

The daughter cells produced in mitosis are genetically identical to the parent
cell and contain the diploid number of chromosomes (46 in humans). In meiosis
the daughter cells are not identical to the parent cell because 'shuffling' of the
genes between homologous chromosomes happens before the first division
(this is called crossing over). The daughter cells produced have one chromatid
from each homologous pair so they are haploid – they contain half the number
of chromosomes in the parent cell (23 in humans).

Q4.   Briefly describe the processes of pollination and fertilisation in plants.

A4.   Pollination is the transmission of pollen – the male gametes – to the stigma
(the female part of the flower). The pollen may be carried by insects or by
the wind.

Once the pollen has reached the stigma a pollen tube grows down into the
ovary, which contains the ovules (the female gametes). Fertilisation is the
fusion of the ovule with the pollen grain to form a zygote.

sensitivity & coordination

Sensitivity

Organisms detect changes in the environment using **receptors**. The receptors detect **stimuli** and **transduce** the energy from a stimulus to form a **nerve impulse**. The receptor is part of a **sense organ**. Organisms must detect and respond to stimuli to survive.

Sense organ	Stimulus	Receptors
Eye	Light	Rods and cones
Ear	Sound Gravity (balance & motion)	Hair cells in the cochlea Semicircular canals
Nose	Smell Taste	Chemical receptors
Tongue	Taste (sour, sweet, bitter, salty)	Taste buds (chemical receptors)
Skin	Touch Pressure Temperature (hot, cold) Pain	Receptive nerve endings

The eye

The structure of the eye is shown on the next page. The **retina** contains the receptor cells and is the part that is sensitive to light. The rest of the eye either protects the retina or focuses light onto it.

The socket of the eye is called the **orbit**. Only the front part of the eye is not surrounded by bone.

The front of the eye is covered by a thin transparent membrane, the **conjunctiva**. This helps to protect the eye. The conjunctiva is kept moist by **tears** which are made in the **tear glands**. Tears contain **lysozyme**, an enzyme that kills and dissolves bacteria. The fluid is washed across the eyes by the **eyelids**, which blink. The eyelids, **eyebrows** and **eyelashes** stop dirt from landing on the eye. The part of the eye that is inside the orbit has a tough coat called the **sclera**. This also protects the eye.

The **choroid** is a black layer behind the retina. It absorbs light after it has passed through the retina, so that light does not get scattered around the inside of the eye.

The **cornea** is a transparent layer at the front of the eye. This is the part of the eye that does most of the focusing. The **lens** does the fine-tuning. The lens becomes thicker or thinner, according to the distance of the object being focused. The lens changes shape by being stretched by the **ciliary muscles**. When the muscles contract, the **suspensory ligaments** become slack, and the lens bulges fat. This allows light from a nearby object to be focused onto the retina. When the muscles relax, the suspensory ligaments become tight, and the lens becomes thinner. This allows light from a faraway object to be focused onto the retina. The adjustment of the shape of the lens is called **accommodation**.

The **iris** consists of two sets of muscles: the **circular muscles** contract to make the **pupil constrict** (get smaller); the **radial muscles** contract to make the pupil **dilate** (get bigger). The pupil dilates in dim light to let more light into the eye; it constricts in strong light to protect the retina.

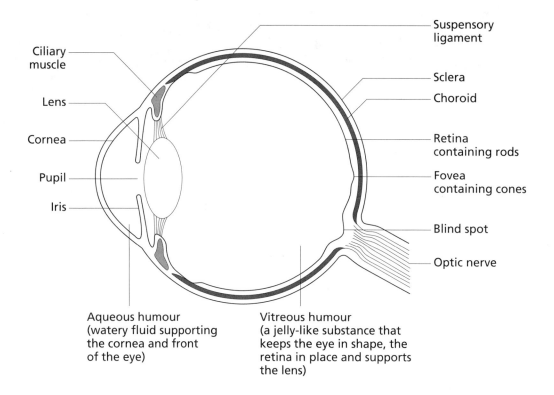

The eye

The receptor cells: rods and cones

Rods are sensitive to dim light, but provide only black and white vision. The rods are distributed right across the retina.

Cones are sensitive only to bright light, and allow colour vision. The cones are concentrated at a point on the retina called the **fovea**. This is on the principal axis of the incoming light rays (if you know any physics). It is the point where the focused light will fall.

There are no receptors where the optic nerve leaves the retina; this is your **blind spot**.

Correcting vision

Short-sightedness

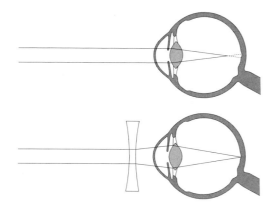

Faraway objects are focused in front of the retina.

This is corrected by a concave lens.

Short-sightedness is caused by the image being *in front of* the retina. The reasons for this may be:

- the eyeball is too long
- the cornea and lens converge the light rays too much.

The person can focus on objects that are nearby, but not on things that are far away.

The correction is a **concave lens** (also called a **diverging** lens). The image is in front of the retina, so a concave lens diverges rays so that they can be converged again correctly by the eye lens and cornea onto the retina.

Long-sightedness

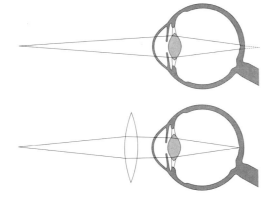

Nearby objects are focused behind the retina.

This is corrected by a convex lens.

Long-sightedness (or **far-sightedness**) is caused because the image is formed *behind* the retina. The reasons for this may be:

- the eyeball is too short
- the cornea and lens do not converge the light rays enough.

The person can focus on things that are far away, but cannot focus on things that are close.

The correction is a **convex lens** (also called a **converging** lens), which helps the lens and the cornea converge the light rays so that the image is formed on the retina, rather than behind it.

As people get older they may develop a problem where the lens gets stiffer, making it harder to pull it into the right shape for focusing. It often gets fixed in a position for focusing distant objects, so reading glasses are needed.

Humans have **binocular vision**: the two images formed by the two eyes overlap and are interpreted into one by the brain. The **parallax effect** allows the brain to produce a three-dimensional image. (Parallax is the effect you see if you look at your finger with one eye, then the other. Each eye sees the finger from a different angle; both views are used by the brain to form a three-dimensional image.)

The Ear

Hearing

The **pinna** (the 'flap' on the outside of your head) and the ear canal gather sound waves. The **tympanum (eardrum)** vibrates, making the **ossicles** vibrate. These three bones (the **malleus** [hammer], **incus** [anvil] and **stapes** [stirrup]) are arranged like a lever, and press against the **oval window** which is a **membrane**.

The oval window is smaller in area than the tympanum, so the pressure is greater on the oval window than on the eardrum (a bit like a hydraulic jack). This means that the sound is *amplified*. Muscles may dampen the vibration of the ossicles to stop damage to the ear.

The air-borne sound vibrations are transmitted to the **perilymph**, the liquid *outside* the **cochlea**. The fluid inside the cochlea, the **endolymph**, begins to vibrate as well. The **hair cells** on the **basilar membranes** inside are pulled and squashed, and impulses travel along the **auditory nerve** to the brain. The hair cells in different parts of the cochlea respond to different vibration frequencies, those nearest the oval window picking up the highest frequencies (highest pitched sounds).

We hear in **stereo**: sound arrives at each ear at slightly different times. The brain uses this information to work out where the sound is coming from.

Balance

Each ear contains three **semicircular canals**, at right angles to each other. Each of the semicircular canals has a bulge at one end. This bulge is called the **ampulla**. Each ampulla has a cone of a jelly-like substance called the **cupula**. The cupula can only move if the head moves in the same plane as its particular semicircular canal.

There are three semicircular canals, and three cupulae in each ear, to sense up and down, left and right, and forwards and backwards movements. If the head moves, then the semicircular canal moves. The cupula moves, and bends the hair cells at its base. Impulses are sent to the brain.

The brain compares the messages from each canal and uses the information to work out how your head is moving, and to help you keep your balance. Your eyes also provide information to help this.

The semicircular canals open into the **utricle**, which connects to the **saccule**. These both contain receptors which provide the brain with information about how the head is tilted, so we know when we are standing up straight.

> *(When the messages from your eyes and ears do not match, you may feel sick. For example if you are reading while travelling in a car.)*

The Eustachian tubes

The eardrum separates the inner and outer ear, both of which are filled with air. If there is a big difference between the pressure inside the ear and the pressure outside the ear, the eardrum may burst. To prevent this happening you swallow: air from the mouth enters the Eustachian tubes (which lead from the middle ear to the back of the throat), and equalises the pressure on either side of the eardrum. This is what is happening when your ears 'pop' as you go up in an aeroplane. (The tubes are usually kept closed by sphincters at the bottom.)

Coordination and response

Just as receptors detect stimuli, **effectors** respond to them. (You can remember this because *effectors* have an *effect*.)

You need some form of **communication** between receptors and effectors so that the right effectors respond in the right way at the right time. The way in which receptors detect stimuli and pass messages to the effectors to respond is called **coordination**.

For example, if you touch something hot, pain receptors in your skin send a message which tells your arm muscles to contract, to move your hand away from the hot surface. This all happens very quickly.

There are two types of communication within the body.

- The **nervous system**, made up of receptors and **nerves**, is the faster of the two.
- The **endocrine system**, made up of receptors and chemicals called **hormones**, is the slower of the two but is just as important.

The nervous system

Nerve impulses are carried by **neurones**. Bundles of neurones form nerves. The diagram overleaf shows that neurones contain the same parts as other animal cells, but the structure is specially *adapted* to carry messages (impulses) quickly.

Dendrons and their branches (**dendrites**) pick up messages from nearby neurones and pass them to the **cell body** and along the **axon**. The axon may pass the message to another neurone, or to an effector.

Some nerve fibres are wrapped in a **myelin sheath**. This is a layer of fat and protein that **insulates** the nerve fibre so that it can carry impulses more quickly. Myelinated fibres carry impulses faster than unmyelinated fibres.

> *(The myelin has gaps called nodes of Ranvier. The impulse jumps from node to node, so fewer nodes means quicker impulse transmission.)*

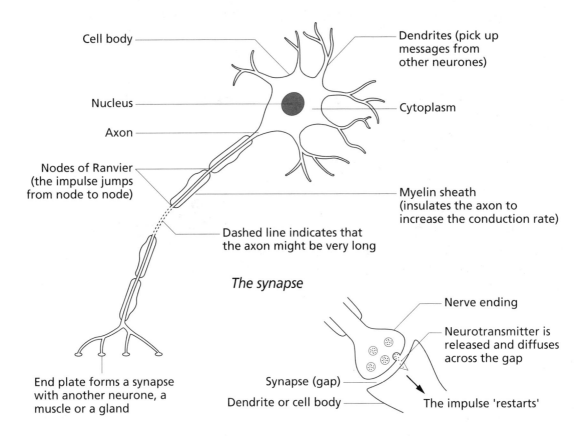

The neurone's structure is specially adapted to its function of transmitting signals quickly over a long distance.

The peripheral nervous system

This is the part of the nervous system that extends to most parts of the body.

The central nervous system

The central nervous system (CNS) consists of the **brain** and the **spinal cord**. The CNS acts as a coordinating centre: nerves in the CNS receive information from receptors and 'decide' which effectors need to respond, when, and how. It then sends appropriate signals to the effector.

Different types of neurone

- **Sensory neurones** carry impulses from receptors to the CNS. They have long dendrons and a short axon.

- **Motor neurones** carry impulses from the CNS to the effector. They have short dendrons and a long axon.

- **Relay neurones** carry impulses between neurones. (I call it an interneurone because I just happen to like it; you should stick with relay neurone because it's the one that GCSE tends to use.)

- **Pyramidal neurones** are found in the CNS. These have many branches, and connect to other pyramidal neurones and relay neurones.

Different neurones 'connect' to each other at **synapses**. The synapse is a small *gap* between the axon of one nerve and the cell body of the next one. The nerve ending contains lots of **vesicles** (bubbles) which contain a chemical called a **neurotransmitter**.

When an impulse comes along the axon, the vesicles empty the neurotransmitter into the synapse. The neurotransmitter diffuses across the gap to receptors on the cell body of the next neurone. This triggers an impulse, and the message is transmitted onwards. Synapses only work in one direction.

Reflex arcs

A **reflex action** is an *automatic response* to a stimulus. It is not a learned response and we don't think about it. This stops time being wasted making decisions. (Hmm, is it really worthwhile for me to remove my hand from this burning hot plate or should I just wait and see if my fingernails melt?)

In reflexes, the brain knows that the response has taken place by the system of relay neurones, but this only happens afterwards. The brain makes no conscious decision in the action itself.

The diagram shows a **reflex arc**: the pathway taken by the nerve impulses.

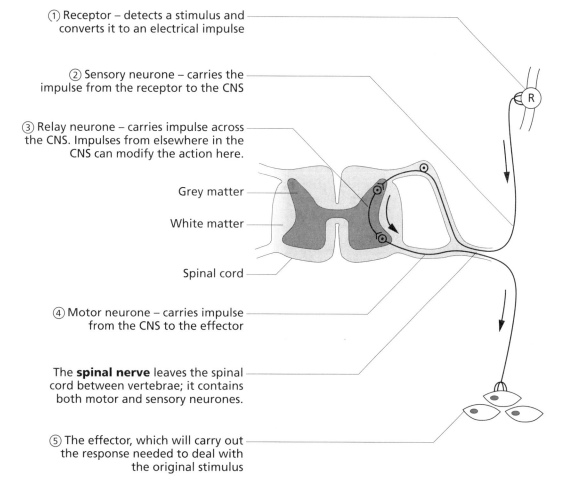

① Receptor – detects a stimulus and converts it to an electrical impulse

② Sensory neurone – carries the impulse from the receptor to the CNS

③ Relay neurone – carries impulse across the CNS. Impulses from elsewhere in the CNS can modify the action here.

Grey matter

White matter

Spinal cord

④ Motor neurone – carries impulse from the CNS to the effector

The **spinal nerve** leaves the spinal cord between vertebrae; it contains both motor and sensory neurones.

⑤ The effector, which will carry out the response needed to deal with the original stimulus

The reflex arc

Why have a complex nervous system?

A complex nervous system allows complex behaviour, as in humans. You can override reflexes. For example, if you pick up a very hot plate, rather than dropping it – the reflex action – you can put it back down gently on a surface so that it doesn't break. You might also decide to hold on to it for a bit longer, even though your fingers hurt, so that you can move somewhere to put it down. The brain considers the options, allowing you to act appropriately. Basically, you can say that actions are modified by earlier experiences. (You know that if you drop the plate it might break, or if you hold on to it for a bit longer that you won't necessarily damage your skin.)

The knee-jerk is also a reflex action; so is blinking when someone waves their hand in front of your face unexpectedly. (I'm sure you can figure out the sequence of events there.) Reflex actions have a *positive survival action*. For example, in bright light the circular muscles of the iris automatically constrict to stop light damaging the retina.

Learned reflexes

These involve the brain. The first person to demonstrate them was Mr Pavlov, who did some experiments with dogs. He devised a way of collecting saliva from a dog's mouth. When the dog smelled food, saliva flowed. This is a reflex action. (The receptor is the nose; the effectors are the salivary glands.) He would ring a bell at the same time as the dogs were smelling food and salivating. After a period of this training, the dogs would salivate when they heard the bell, even if they couldn't smell food. This is a learned reflex.

Learned reflexes are things that you learn by *practice* and then become *second nature*. Riding a bike is an example: you don't need to think about how to do it, or how to keep your balance.

Conscious action

Sensory information travels to the brain which processes it before action. Consciousness allows scope for intelligence. (Or at least, that's what humans say to make them feel good about themselves.)

Some actions, like breathing, are both **involuntary** and **conscious**: most of the time you don't think about breathing. However, when you are swimming under water you can consciously control your breathing, but eventually the automatic control mechanisms override the voluntary action.

The brain

The brain functions are **localised**; vision is coordinated in one place, hearing in another, touch in another, etc. The brain is protected by membranes called the **meninges**.

- The largest part of the brain is the wrinkly part called the **cerebrum**. It consists of two halves, each being a **cerebral hemisphere**. Humans have the largest cerebral hemispheres of all mammals relative to the size of the rest of the brain (although we don't use more than a third of them at any one time). Conscious thought and memory occur in the cerebrum. An area near the front of the cerebrum determines some parts of your personality.

- The **olfactory lobes** are for smell, and these project forwards from the brain, partly into the nose.

- The **hypothalamus** is under the front part of the cerebrum. This controls **osmoregulation** (water regulation) and temperature regulation. (See page 101).

- The **cerebellum** coordinates movements and balance.

- The **medulla oblongata** deals with tasks like heart rate, the control of blood flow, and breathing.

The endocrine system

Endocrine glands make hormones. The hormones are released into blood vessels inside the gland. The endocrine gland therefore needs no **ducts**, as opposed to **exocrine** glands which do have ducts (e.g. the tear gland and tear duct; the salivary glands and salivary duct).

Hormones are **chemical messengers**. They are secreted into the bloodstream, which carries them to their destination. Hormones usually break down easily, so they do not remain in the blood for too long. Hormones therefore have to be produced continually. Each hormone only affects certain parts of the body – the cells that have the right carrier protein or receptor on their cell surface membrane.

Adrenaline

Adrenaline is secreted from the **adrenal glands**, situated above the kidneys. It makes the heart beat faster when more energy is required to either fight or run away (also called **fight or flight**). It makes the blood vessels in the skin constrict, so you go pale, and also in the digestive system causing 'butterflies in the stomach'. Blood is diverted to the muscles and the brain, delivering more oxygen.

Adrenaline needs to be produced constantly for a long-lasting effect. Its production is stimulated when you feel frightened or excited. The stimulus is received from the nervous system, so the glands are quick to secrete adrenaline when needed.

Thyroxine

Thyroxine is produced by the **thyroid gland**. It is secreted all the time but in small amounts. It regulates the rate at which the mitochondria respire, and so controls the **metabolic rate**. If not enough thyroxine is produced, a child doesn't grow properly and the brain doesn't develop properly. This is called **cretinism**; it can be treated with thyroxine injections.

If adults lack thyroxine, they become overweight and sluggish. If they have too much thyroxine, they become thin, hyperactive and touchy.

Thyroxine contains iodine. If there is not enough iodine in the diet, the thyroid gland cannot make enough thyroxine and swells up to compensate for this. This condition is called a **goitre**.

Androgens

Androgens are the male sex hormones. The most important androgen is called **testosterone**. This regulates sexual development in males. At puberty (12–14 years) the boy becomes sexually mature and sperm production begins. Testosterone also controls development of the secondary sexual characteristics: facial and pubic hair grows, the voice breaks and muscular development begins.

Oestrogens

Oestrogens control sexual development in females. Ovulation begins at puberty (which is slightly earlier in girls), and the menstrual cycle begins. (See topic nine.) The sex organs develop, along with the secondary sexual characteristics: pubic hair grows, breasts develop and the pelvic girdle widens.

Insulin

Insulin is made in the **islets of Langerhans** in the pancreas. It is secreted when the blood glucose level is too high. It causes the liver and muscles to take up glucose and store it as glycogen. **Diabetes** is the condition in which insufficient insulin is produced. (See page 103.)

Glucagon

Glucagon is also produced in the islets of Langerhans in the pancreas. It is secreted when the blood glucose level is too low. It causes the liver and muscles to break down glycogen to release glucose.

$$\text{Glucose} \quad \underset{\text{Glucagon}}{\overset{\text{Insulin}}{\rightleftarrows}} \quad \text{Glycogen}$$

(Note: Don't mix up glucagon and glycogen, and don't mix up the functions of insulin and glucagon. Try: 'Secrete glucagon when the glucose has gone.' It's pathetic, but it works!)

Antidiuretic hormone

Antidiuretic hormone (ADH) is secreted by the pituitary gland when the water content in the blood is too low. It causes the kidneys to reabsorb water. ADH secretion is inhibited by alcohol, so drinking too much alcohol causes dehydration. (See page 101.) (A **diuretic** is a chemical, like caffeine, that causes diuresis, 'watery urine'.)

Thyroid stimulating hormone

As its name suggests, **thyroid stimulating hormone** stimulates the thyroid gland to produce thyroxine. It is secreted from the pituitary gland throughout life.

Growth hormone

Growth hormone is secreted by the pituitary gland throughout life and especially during the 'growth spurt'. Lack of growth hormone causes **dwarfism**; too much causes **gigantism**.

The pituitary gland

The pituitary gland is the 'emperor gland', the other endocrine glands being its slaves and minions. The pituitary, however, is not at the top of the pyramid; it is controlled by nerve messages from the hypothalamus, which makes it secrete hormones such as ADH. In this case, receptors in the hypothalamus sense that there is not enough water in the blood. The hypothalamus then sends signals to the pituitary gland telling it to release ADH. ADH acts in the kidneys so that water is reabsorbed rather than being lost in the urine (see topic eleven).

Summary

Nervous system	Endocrine system
• Neurones	• Endocrine glands
• Messages transmitted as 'electrical' impulses along nerve fibres	• Messages transmitted by hormones (chemicals) released into the bloodstream
• Very fast	• Slower
• Short-term effects	• Longer term effects

Tropisms – coordination in plants

Plants can respond to stimuli by growing in different directions. A **tropism** is the tendency of a plant to grow towards or away from a certain stimulus. We will deal with two types of tropism: **phototropism** and **geotropism**.

Positive phototropism is when the plant grows towards light. ('Photo' means light.) This happens in the **plumule** (shoot). **Negative phototropism** is when a plant grows away from light. This may happen in some **radicles** (roots), but usually there is *neutral* tropism. If a plant always receives light from the same side, it will always grow towards the light, resulting in a lopsided plant.

Positive geotropism is where the plant grows towards the pull of gravity. This happens in the radicle. **Negative geotropism** is where the plant grows away from the pull of gravity. This happens in the plumule.

So, as you can see, the plumule (shoot) always grows in the opposite direction to the radicle (root). The shoots need to grow away from gravity and towards the light for photosynthesis. (Remember how leaves are always held out to the sunlight.)

The roots have to grow downwards to anchor the plant firmly in the soil and to absorb water and take up minerals.

Phototropism in coleoptiles

A **coleoptile** is a protective sheath covering the first leaf of grain seedlings.

The growth of plant is controlled by **growth hormones**. One type of growth hormone is called **auxin**. We will deal with tropisms in terms of auxin only.

In shoots, auxin promotes growth; in roots, auxin inhibits growth. It is made in the tip of the coleoptile, and diffuses down it.

The tip of the coleoptile is sensitive to light. The part of the plant just below the tip is the part that grows. Phototropisms can be explained by considering the changes in auxin concentrations. Auxins make the cells just behind the tip get longer. Without auxin there is no growth; the more auxin there is, the faster the growth. When light shines on one side of the shoot, auxin accumulates on the shaded side. The cells on this side grow faster than the cells on the sunny side, so the tip grows towards the light.

Although auxin stimulates growth of the shoot tip, it inhibits the growth of side shoots so that the plant grows tall and straight. If you cut off the top of the plant, the flow of auxin stops and side shoots will grow, making the plant bushier. (Gardeners do this to get bushy plants or thick hedges.)

Use of plant hormones in agriculture

Plant hormones can be used to:

- increase yield from plants
- speed up growth
- speed up formation of new plants
- improve the look of plants and gardens.

Weedkillers often contain a type of auxin. The weedkillers are often **selective** so that the weeds in a lawn are killed, but not the grass. The weeds respond by growing quickly for a few days but then they die.

Fruit growers often use hormones to make fruit grow larger or ripen quicker. Many fruits produce **ethene** (a gas) as they ripen. Fruit can be picked while it is unripe. Once it has been transported, it can be exposed to ethene so that it ripens. Bananas release a lot of ethene, which is why the other fruit ripens quickly if there are bananas in the bowl.

Gardeners use **rooting powder** to help shoot cuttings grow. The cut end of the stem is dipped in the powder, which contains **growth substances**; these stimulate roots to grow.

Worked questions

Q1. *What is long-sightedness? How is it corrected?*

A1. In long-sightedness the image forms behind the retina either because the eyeball is too short or because the lens and cornea can't converge the light rays enough to focus the image onto the retina. This means it is hard to focus on objects that are nearby.

Long-sightedness is corrected by putting a convex lens in front of the eye, which helps to converge the light rays onto the retina.

Q2. *Which structures in the ear help with balance? Describe how they work.*

A2. The semicircular canals in the ear are important for balance. There are three in each ear at right angles to each other to detect up and down, side to side, and forwards and backwards movements. Each semicircular canal has a bulge at one end called the ampulla which contains a cone of jelly-like substance called the cupula. When the cupula moves, hair cells at its base are bent. This information goes to the brain, which uses it to work out how your head is moving so that you can keep your balance.

Q3. *What are the functions of the sensory and motor neurones? Describe the differences in their structure in terms of dendrites and axons.*

A3. Sensory neurones carry impulses from receptors in the periphery to the central nervous system (CNS). They have long dendrites and a short axon.

Motor neurones carry impulses from the CNS to the effector (the part of the body that will carry out the response). They have short dendrites and a long axon.

Q4. *Describe the chain of events when you stand on a drawing pin.*

A4. Nerve endings in your foot detect pain. Impulses travel via a sensory neurone to your brain and, via a reflex arc, impulses come back via a motor neurone to make you move your foot off the sharp object (to prevent damage). Impulses go elsewhere in the brain so that it knows what has happened.

Q5. *Give three differences between the endocrine system and the nervous system.*

A5. The nervous system is involved with short-term effects and acts quickly. Messages (impulses) are transmitted via neurones. The endocrine system is involved with long-term effects and acts slowly. Messages are transmitted via hormones which are chemicals released into the blood.

Q6. *Why do gardeners pinch out the top of plants to encourage bushy growth?*

A6. Growth in the shoot tip is controlled by a hormone called auxin; this hormone inhibits growth of side shoots. By pinching out the tip, the auxin is also removed, so side shoots can grow, making a bushier plant.

homeostasis & excretion

Homeostasis

Homeostasis   keeping the internal environment of an organism constant

The outside environment is changing continuously, but some organisms keep their internal environment remarkably constant. In homeostasis the body's systems work together so that all cells are provided with optimum conditions to function as efficiently as possible. For example, homeostasis keeps the amount of water constant so that cells do not take in or lose too much by osmosis. It controls body temperature (keeping it at about 37°C) for enzymes in metabolic reactions. It also keeps a constant amount of glucose available for respiration.

Homeostasis works by **negative feedback.** This is a simple **control system**. A generalised negative feedback loop is shown in the diagram. Negative feedback is feedback that switches off the action.

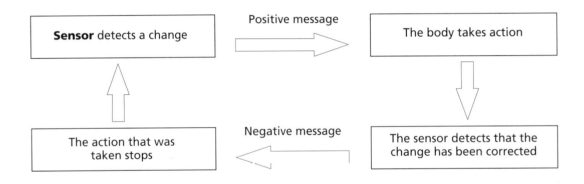

For example, the thermostat in a central heating system detects that the temperature in the room is too low. It sends a signal to switch the heater on. The thermostat detects when the room temperature is high enough (i.e. information about the temperature is *fed back* to the thermostat) and switches the heater off (i.e. tells it to stop doing what it was doing). There are many examples of negative feedback loops in biological systems.

Osmoregulation

Osmoregulation   maintenance of a constant water level in the blood

- Cells in the **hypothalamus** detect if water levels in the blood are too low.

- The hypothalamus sends a signal to the **pituitary gland** to release **antidiuretic hormone (ADH)** into the blood. This is the positive action.

- The ADH acts on the **kidney** so that water is reabsorbed.

- When water levels are normal again, a negative signal is sent from the hypothalamus to the pituitary gland telling it to stop secreting ADH.

If the water level in the blood becomes too high (e.g. after a drink) the hypothalamus tells the pituitary gland to stop secreting ADH, so that water is not reabsorbed by the kidney and you produce more dilute **urine**.

If we plot water level against time, we get a wavy line: the overall level stays constant. This is called a **dynamic equilibrium**.

As well as keeping the water content of the blood constant, the body must balance water entering and leaving the body. The colon and the kidney both reabsorb water to prevent wastage; fine tuning is done by the kidney. **Thirst** is a mechanism that makes you take in water if you need it (for example after exercise, or when you sweat a lot). (We go into the kidneys in more detail on page 105.)

> *(Alcohol confuses the osmoregulation system because it stops the release of ADH. This means that your body continues to act as though it has too much water. Water is not reabsorbed by the kidneys so even though you may have drunk a large volume of liquid, you end up feeling dehydrated.)*

Thermoregulation

Mammals and birds have the ability to keep their internal body temperature constant, regardless of the external temperature. They are said to be **homeothermic**.

Reptiles cannot do this; they are **poikilothermic**. They are only active when the outside temperature is high; if it is too high, they move into the shade to prevent overheating. Their activity very much depends on external conditions, whereas homeothermic animals can still be active in the cold.

Thermoregulation in humans

Cells in the hypothalamus detect changes in the body's core temperature. If the temperature is too high, it sends signals to various parts of the body to take action so that heat is lost. The skin is the main organ involved in temperature regulation.

- The **erector muscles** in the skin relax so that the hair lies flat and no longer traps warmth. This allows more heat to be lost by radiation.

- The muscles in the arterioles in the skin relax so that blood flows into the surface capillaries. (This is **vasodilation**; it explains why you go red when you are hot.) Heat is lost from the blood at the surface.

- The **sweat glands** start to secrete **sweat**, which is a watery fluid made from plasma. It is mostly water but contains some salt and urea. The sweat flows onto the skin via the **sweat ducts** and evaporates, taking *latent* heat from the surroundings and cooling the skin.

  Sweating is the only way we have of making our body temperature lower than the outside temperature. It is important that you drink plenty to replace the fluid lost by sweating. (This is why you feel thirsty in hot weather.)

We also display **behavioural** responses: changing our clothes, moving into the shade or being less active so we generate less heat.

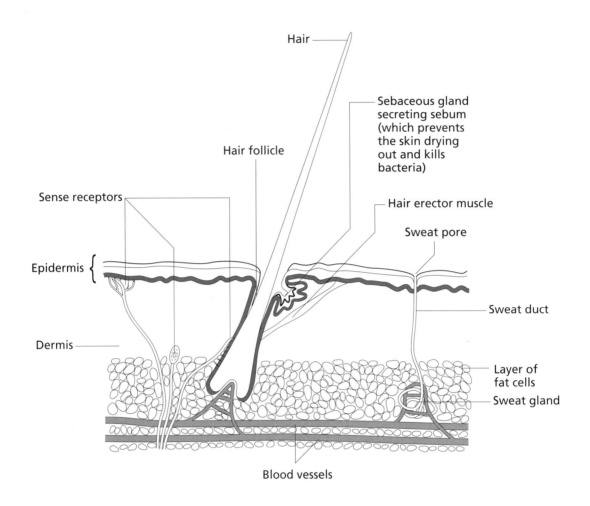

The structure of human skin showing the parts involved in temperature regulation

If the body temperature is too low, this is detected by the hypothalamus, which sends signals to the skin and other parts of the body to generate more heat and prevent heat loss.

- The erector muscles connected to the hair follicles contract, making the hairs stand on end. This traps pockets of air which act as a layer of insulation, preventing heat loss. This is very effective in furry animals. Humans just get goose bumps, which are useless!

- **Vasoconstriction** occurs: the muscles of the arterioles constrict, decreasing blood flow to the skin surface and decreasing heat loss from the skin. This explains why your skin goes cold and pale, even though your blood is warm.

- Muscles contract and relax randomly. This is **shivering**, which generates heat.

- The metabolic activity of the liver increases, generating heat. (This is why you are hungrier in cold than in hot weather.)

- Behavioural changes include moving into a warmer place, putting on more clothes and becoming more active.

This system is fairly efficient and body temperature stays pretty constant. However, it is not always possible to maintain body temperature in extreme conditions. When someone's body temperature falls well below normal, they are said to have **hypothermia**. They are no longer able to generate enough heat to keep their temperature up. People suffering from hypothermia should be wrapped in warm, dry clothing and given hot drinks.

Regulation of blood glucose

Glucose is needed by all cells for respiration. It is therefore important that the concentration of glucose in the blood is kept fairly constant. Brain cells in particular die very quickly if they don't get enough glucose.

The **pancreas** and **liver** control glucose levels using the hormones **insulin** and **glucagon**.

The **islets of Langerhans** in the pancreas detect glucose levels. If they are too high, the islets secrete insulin. Insulin makes the liver take up glucose and convert it to glycogen which is stored. When blood glucose levels are too low, glucagon is secreted, making the liver convert glycogen into glucose, which is released into the blood. (See page 96 for a useful mnemonic to remember this.)

Diabetes mellitus

Lack of insulin leads to a condition called **diabetes mellitus** (sugar diabetes); the liver does not take up glucose. Too much glucose in the blood (hyperglycaemia) can damage the brain cells and could lead to coma and death.

The extra glucose is passed into the urine. Healthy people have no glucose in the urine. People used to test for diabetes by tasting the urine, to see if it was sweet. (This is where the mellitus in diabetes mellitus comes from, mellitus meaning honey.) Fortunately, biosensors are used nowadays (see page 19).

If there is a shortage of insulin, the glycogen stores get used up, and this leads to a lack of glucose in the blood: **hypoglycaemia**. This can also lead to coma and eventually death.

The best way to treat someone who is hypoglycaemic is to give them a sweet drink or sugary foods like chocolate bars. Starchy foods like potatoes are not useful in such an urgent situation because it takes a long time for them to be broken down to release glucose.

Diabetes can be controlled by taking daily injections of insulin, or in milder cases, by regulating the amount of carbohydrate in the diet.

Excretion

Excretion   the removal of waste substances

Some of this waste is **toxic**. In humans, there are three excretory substances.

- **Carbon dioxide** is produced by all living cells from respiration; it is removed from the blood via the **alveoli** and **exhaled** (breathed out).

- **Bile pigments** are made in the liver from the remains of old red blood cells. The iron from the haemoglobin is stored, and the pigments are excreted in the **faeces**.
- **Urea** is also made in the liver. It is made from excess proteins, and is transported to the kidneys to be excreted. Urea is **nitrogenous** waste.

Excretory products in plants

The excretory products in plants are slightly different to those in humans.

- *Oxygen* is the waste product of photosynthesis; it is excreted during the day via the stomata in the leaves. (Some of it is used for respiration.)
- *Carbon dioxide* is the waste product of respiration; it is excreted at night via the stomata. (During the day it is used for photosynthesis.)
- Plants have no nitrogenous waste because they make their own proteins and so they can make as much or as little as they need.
- Any other substances that are not wanted accumulate in the leaves. These substances are lost when the leaves fall off.

Excretion in animals
Deamination of excess protein

Protein that is eaten is digested into peptides and then into amino acids. These are absorbed from the ileum and go to the liver in the hepatic portal vein. Some of the amino acids are used. The excess cannot be stored. It would be wasteful for the body to excrete amino acids because the carbon, hydrogen and oxygen can be converted to carbohydrate or fat for energy.

Enzymes in the liver remove the nitrogenous component as **ammonia**. This is very toxic and is quickly converted to urea. Urea dissolves in the blood and is excreted by the kidneys. (A little bit is excreted in sweat.)

The reactions are:

Amino acid $\rightarrow$ carbohydrate + ammonia

Ammonia + carbon dioxide $\rightarrow$ urea + water

$$2NH_3 + CO_2 \rightarrow CO(NH_2)_2 + H_2O$$

The liver

The liver has a large number of functions, many of which are important for homeostasis. Some of the functions are listed below:

- deamination
- controlling glucose levels in the blood
- storage of polysaccharides (like glycogen) and vitamins (A, D)
- breakdown of old red blood cells; storing iron from haemoglobin

- breakdown of nasty stuff like alcohol
- making bile (see digestion; topic four)
- making cholesterol, which is needed to construct cell membranes
- generating heat by performing all these metabolic reactions.

The kidneys

The kidneys are the main organs responsible for excretion. There are two, one on each side of the body; they are situated below the diaphragm, behind the intestines.

The kidney has three main parts: the outside is the **cortex** and the inside is the **medulla**. The middle of the kidney is the **pelvis**. The urine made by the kidney drains from here into a tube called the **ureter**. The ureter from each kidney goes to the **bladder**.

The kidney contains thousands of tiny **tubules** called **nephrons**; this is where the urine is made.

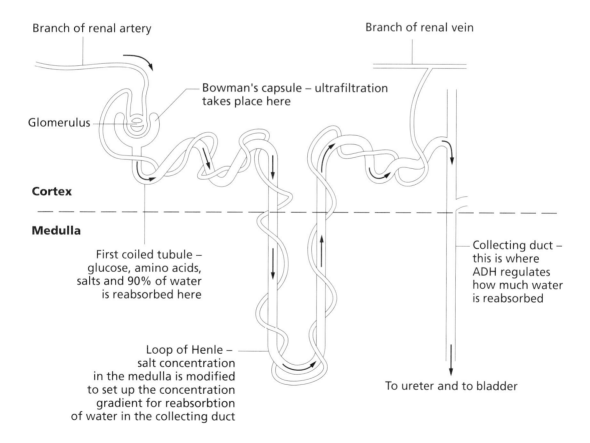

The nephron and its function

At the start of each tubule is the **Bowman's capsule**. In its cavity there is a bundle of blood capillaries called the **glomerulus** which contains oxygenated blood from the renal artery. This part of each nephron is in the cortex of the kidney. A long loop called the **loop of Henle** from each nephron extends into the medulla. From the loop of Henle the nephron goes back into the cortex and then back out through the medulla to the pelvis. The nephrons join up with the ureter in the pelvis.

Formation of urine

The strange structure of the nephron is specially adapted to **filter** the blood, removing waste materials, but returning useful materials to the blood. This is done by **ultrafiltration** followed by **reabsorption**.

The blood vessel going into the glomerulus is wider than the one going out. This means that the pressure in the glomerulus is high. The walls of both the glomerulus and the Bowman's capsule have tiny holes. Water, salts, sugar, amino acids and urea are forced out of the blood into the nephron; proteins and blood cells are too large to get through, so they stay in the blood. The walls of the capillary and Bowman's capsule are acting as **partially permeable membranes**. Ultrafiltration means diffusion aided by pressure.

As the fluid flows along the rest of the nephron, useful materials (sugar, amino acids, some water, some minerals) are reabsorbed into capillaries that surround the nephron. Water is reabsorbed by **osmosis**; other materials are taken up by **active transport**.

The kidneys *regulate* the amount of water that is reabsorbed, and the pH of the blood by controlling absorption of hydrogen ions and salts.

By the time the fluid reaches the **collecting duct** it is mostly water with urea and salts dissolved in it. This is urine. It flows into the ureters and then into the bladder where it is stored. The wall of the bladder is quite stretchy so that it can hold quite a lot of urine.

The tube leading out of the bladder is the **urethra** which is kept closed by a **sphincter** at the top. Adult mammals have **voluntary control** of this sphincter, so they can decide when to urinate. Young animals can't do this; the bladder empties when it is full.

Kidney failure

A person's kidneys may stop working because of damage or an infection. You can live with about one third of a kidney still working. If the kidneys fail completely, waste and other materials build up in the blood and the amount of water in the body is not regulated properly. The patient will die unless they are treated.

Dialysis
The most common treatment is with a **dialysis machine**, which filters the blood. Blood from the artery in the patient's arm flows into the machine and through a **dialyser**.

- The dialyser contains dialysis fluid which has salts and other substances dissolved in it at normal blood concentrations.

- The fluid is separated from the patient's blood by a partially permeable membrane.

- The concentration of urea is higher in the blood than the dialysis fluid (which doesn't contain any) so urea diffuses out of the blood.

- The dialysis fluid contains sugars and salts at optimum concentration. These substances will diffuse into or out of the blood until the concentrations are balanced.

- The blood and dialysis fluid flow in *opposite* directions – this is called a **counter current** – so that the concentration gradients for diffusion are maintained.

Patients have to be treated with dialysis for a few hours at a time, two or three times a week. Although some patients have a dialysis machine at home, most have to go to hospital for the treatment, which can be very inconvenient. Patients also have to be careful about what they eat so that waste products don't build up too quickly.

Kidney transplant
The alternative to dialysis is to have a kidney transplant, in which a kidney from a **donor** is transplanted into the patient. The donor might be someone who has died, or a close family member like a brother or sister. (You only need one kidney to stay healthy, which is why you can afford to give one to someone else.)

The patient has to take **immunosuppressant drugs**. These stop the immune system from attacking the transplanted kidney, which would lead to **rejection** (see pages 7 and 65). The drugs can have unpleasant side-effects and the patient is at risk of infection because the immune system can't work properly.

A successful transplant can last 10 years and allows the patient to live a normal life, rather than going into hospital all the time for dialysis.

Worked questions

Q1. Define the term homeostasis.

A1. Homeostasis is the maintenance of a constant, regular internal environment.

Q2. How does your body respond if your core temperature is too high?

A2. Cells in the hypothalamus detect core temperature and initiate responses to modify it. The erector muscles in the skin relax so that the hairs lie flat and don't trap air. The capillaries in the skin dilate so that heat can be lost from the blood at the skin surface. The sweat glands produce sweat, which evaporates from the skin surface, cooling the skin by taking latent heat from the surroundings. Behavioural responses also help: moving away from the source of the heat and removing clothing.

Q3. Describe the roles of insulin and glucagon.

A3. Glucagon and insulin regulate the level of glucose in the blood. If the level is too low, glucagon is released which converts glycogen in the liver to glucose.

If the concentration of glucose in the blood is high, insulin is released which stimulates the conversion of glucose to glycogen for storage.

Q4. *Explain how the kidney produces urine.*

A4. The blood in the glomerulus is at high pressure. The plasma (but none of the cells) diffuses under pressure into the Bowman's capsule. This is ultrafiltration. Useful substances (glucose, amino acids, salts, water) are reabsorbed from the nephron. The remaining fluid contains water, salts and urea; this is urine. The kidney regulates how much salt and water is reabsorbed; the remainder stays in the urine.

Q5. *In a dialysis machine, the patient's blood flows through special tubing bathed in dialysis fluid. State one difference and two similarities between the dialysis fluid and the patient's plasma.*

A5. The dialysis fluid contains more water than plasma and doesn't contain urea or protein.

The dialysis fluid is at the same temperature as plasma and has the same concentrations of glucose and salts as normal plasma. Any excess in the plasma diffuses into the dialysis fluid.

support & movement

The skeleton

An organism's body is supported by its **skeleton**. Humans have an **endoskeleton**; it is inside the body. Insects have an **exoskeleton**; it is outside the body.

The human skeleton is made of **bone** which contains protein, and minerals such as **calcium phosphate** and **magnesium salts**. These make it very hard. It also contains **collagen**, which is a protein, and provides elasticity. The bone is *living tissue*; it contains living cells. These are found in concentric rings around the blood vessels.

The outside of the bone is called the **compact bone**. It is the hard part. Underneath the compact bone is the **spongy bone**, which has spaces in it making the bone lighter. The centre of the bone is the **bone marrow**, which is soft, and has a good blood supply. The marrow makes red blood cells, white blood cells and platelets.

The ends of a bone are covered with **cartilage**. This has less of the mineral salts and more of the collagen than bone. It allows the bones to **articulate** (move) with each other smoothly, without abrasion.

The human skeleton:

- supports the body   (spine, pelvis, leg bones)
- allows it to move   (leg and arm bones)
- gives it protection   (skull, ribs)
- makes blood cells   (bone marrow of ribs and leg bones).

You don't need to know the names of all the bones in the body (thankfully). The ones to remember are:

- femur   (thigh)
- pelvis   (hip)
- humerus   (upper arm)
- radius   (forearm, thumb side)
- ulna   (forearm, little finger side).

Joints

Joints are where two bones meet each other. There are two types: **fibrous** and **synovial** joints.

Fibrous joints are found between **vertebrae** in the spine and in the **cranium** of the skull. The bones of the cranium are held together very tightly by **fibres** called **sutures**, so that they cannot actually move. Vertebrae are held together by **intervertebral discs** which are pieces of cartilage with fibres in it. The cartilage is quite soft in the middle so the vertebrae can move a little bit. The spine is quite flexible because of the sum effect of all these small movements.

Synovial joints

The diagram shows the human elbow, which is an example of a synovial joint.

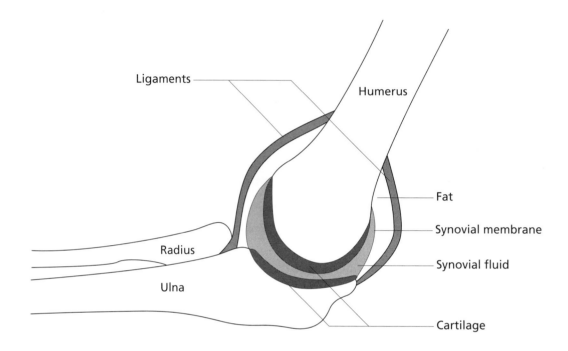

The elbow is a synovial joint; it connects the humerus of the upper arm with the ulna of the forearm.

The two bones, the humerus and the ulna, need to move freely so there is no abrasive damage. The cartilage on the end of each bone provides this protection. The bones are held together by strong but elastic structures called **ligaments**. The joint is lubricated by the oily **synovial fluid** which is secreted by the **synovial membrane**.

The elbow is a **hinge joint**: it allows movement in one plane only, up and down, or, if you are holding your arm sideways, left and right. (You can twist your wrist, but there is no movement at the elbow joint, it is just the radius and ulna twisting around each other.)

Ball and socket joints allow movement in all planes. This type of joint is exactly as the name implies: a ball in a socket. The hip is an example of a ball and socket joint.

Arthritis

In **arthritis**, the cartilage covering the ends of the bones is damaged, making it painful and difficult to move.

Badly damaged joints can be replaced with artificial joints. Hip joints are replaced most often; shoulder, knee and finger joints can also be replaced.

The replacement joint must be made of material that doesn't corrode when it comes into contact with body fluids. It must be strong and have smooth surfaces to allow easy movement. It must also be made of a material that the body won't react with, otherwise it would cause inflammation and pain.

Muscles

There are three types of muscle in humans.

Cardiac muscle is only found in the heart. It contracts rhythmically, non-stop, without getting tired. This muscle will contract by itself – it doesn't need messages from the brain to stimulate contraction. Nerve impulses from the brain tell it how fast to contract.

Smooth muscle is found in organs such as the bladder and the alimentary canal. Some types of smooth muscle can contract of their own accord – as in the muscles involved in peristalsis. In other places, smooth muscle is stimulated by nerves. Smooth muscle is sometimes called **involuntary** muscle because you don't have conscious control over it. Smooth muscle contracts and relaxes slowly and rhythmically.

Striated muscle looks striped under the microscope, hence its name. All the muscles attached to bones are striated. They are also called **skeletal** or **voluntary** muscles because they are under conscious control. They only contract when they receive nerve impulses. This type of muscle can contract strongly and quickly but gets tired more quickly than the other types of muscle. The muscles are joined to the bones by groups of collagen fibres called **tendons**. These are strong and do not stretch easily (although too much tension can snap them).

How muscles contract

Muscle contains fibres called **fibrils** made of two types of protein: **actin** and **myosin**. The myosin **filaments** lie in between the actin filaments. The filaments slide between each other, making the muscle shorter.

You can visualise this by placing the fingers of each hand between each other, with the fingernails lined up. Now slide your fingers in between each other and squeeze. This represents the muscle contracting.

Bonds are made between the actin and myosin. The energy needed to form these bands comes from the breakdown of ATP. Bonds are made, broken and remade as the filaments slide past each other. When the fibres stop moving, more and more bonds form, making the grip stronger. You need energy even if the muscles aren't actually moving, to keep the muscles contracted. This demand for energy explains why muscles need such a good blood supply.

Movement

Muscles work in **antagonistic pairs**. This means that for each movement, there are two muscles involved. One moves the bone one way, the other moves it back. We will look at the movement of the forearm (see diagram). To **extend** the arm (straighten it), the **triceps** contracts, pulling up on the ulna. The **biceps** relaxes, relieving the force on the radius. The forearm is extended. The triceps is an **extensor muscle**.

To **flex** the arm (bend it at the elbow), the biceps contracts, pulling up on the radius. The triceps relaxes, relieving the force on the ulna. The forearm is flexed. The biceps is a **flexor** muscle.

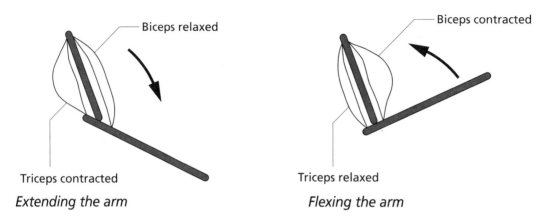

Extending the arm

Flexing the arm

Note that muscles can only cause movement by *contracting*, not relaxing. Relaxing one muscle simply allows the other muscle in the antagonistic pair to contract.

Cilia

Cilia are microscopic hair-like threads that move. You have cilia in your trachea and bronchi which beat rhythmically. This wafts mucus with trapped dirt and bacteria up to your mouth to be swallowed. Cilia also waft the follicle along the Fallopian tube.

Many **single-celled** organisms use cilia to move around. These organisms, which belong to the phylum **Protoctista**, live in water and feed on bacteria and other protoctists. *Paramecium* is one example. The covering of cilia beats rhythmically pushing it through the water.

Amoeboid movement

Amoeba is also a protoctist but moves around by **amoeboid movement**. A particular part of the cell pushes out to produce a **pseudopodium** (pseudo: false; podium: foot) and the whole cell gradually flows in the same direction. Pseudopodia are pushed out in different places to change directions. This type of movement is slower than using cilia but is useful for moving over surfaces like mud.

White blood cells also move by amoeboid movement, allowing them to squeeze into all parts of the body.

Adaptations for support and movement

Birds

Birds are adapted for flying.

- The bones contain large air spaces making them light.

- The forelimbs (upper limbs) have become wings. Strong muscles pull the wing bones up and down. The muscles are attached to the sternum – called the **keel** in birds – which is enlarged.

- The wings act as **aerofoils**: the upper surface is curved and the lower surface is flat. Air travels more quickly over the upper surface so the air pressure below the wing is higher than above it. This provides **lift**.

- The body is covered with **feathers**. These provide a large surface area, keeping the bird in the air, and provide insulation.

- The bird is **streamlined** – its shape means that it cuts cleanly through the air. The feathers lie against the body so air flows easily over them.

Fish

Fish are adapted for swimming.

- They have a **flexible vertebral column**. This allows the fish's body to curve from side to side to produce forward motion.

- They have an air-filled bladder, called a **swim bladder**, just below the vertebral column. The amount of air in it is adjusted so the fish swims at the right depth.

- Fish don't need as strong a skeleton as mammals because the water supports their weight.

- Fish are streamlined so that they cut easily through the water. The scales overlap and point backwards so water flows over them. They also produce **mucus** from a thin transparent skin; this reduces **drag**.

- **Fins** help the fish balance in the water and help with **propulsion** (the **caudal** fin does anyway).

- The tail also helps with propulsion.

Insects

Insects have an exoskeleton. Areas of the exoskeleton that need to be hard and rigid are made of a mixture of **chitin** and protein. Areas that need to be flexible (at the joints, on the wings) are made of just chitin.

The exoskeleton is covered with a **cuticle**, a waxy substance that stops water evaporating from the insect's body.

Earthworms

Earthworms do not have a hard exo- or endoskeleton. The fluid inside them holds them in shape – this is called a **hydrostatic skeleton**.

Earthworms move through burrows. Mucus on their skin helps to protect against damage. They move using **longitudinal** and **circular** muscles, which work antagonistically, and bristles, called **chaetae**, on their underside, which help grip the sides of the burrow.

To move, the circular muscles at the back of the worm contract, squeezing the front of the worm forwards; the chaetae at the front withdraw and those at the back dig into the soil, holding the back of the worm still. Then, the longitudinal muscles at the front contract, pulling the back of the worm forwards; the front chaetae dig in while the back ones withdraw.

Plants

Okay, so plants don't move much (although **tropism** [page 97] is a movement
of sorts).

Plants do need a support system. Large plants have **lignin** in the cell walls of the
xylem vessels to provide support. Trees have woody trunks and branches, which are
made of dense lignified material.

Leaves and **herbaceous** plants do not have lignin; they are held up by cell **turgor**:
the water in the plant's cells pushes against the cell walls, making the cell **turgid** (firm)
and the cells push against each other, holding the plant firm and upright. When cells
lose water, they lose this turgor and the leaves wilt. The main stem is held up by
xylem vessels and lignified cells, so it doesn't wilt.

Worked questions

Q1. *Which two muscles are involved in the flexing and extension of the forearm?*

A1. The biceps is involved in flexing the forearm; the triceps is involved in extending it.

Q2. *When the forearm is lifted up (flexed), which muscle CONTRACTS, and which
muscle RELAXES?*

A2. When the forearm is flexed the biceps contracts and the triceps relaxes.

Q3. *What type of joint is the elbow joint? Name the fluid in the joint and explain
its function.*

A3. The elbow is a synovial joint. It is also a hinged joint. The fluid is called synovial
fluid. Its function is to lubricate the joint so that the humerus can move against
the radius smoothly.

Q4. *Describe how plants are supported.*

A4. Large plants like trees have lignin in the cell walls of the xylem. This is a dense
woody material that provides support. Smaller plants are held up by turgor:
the vacuoles in the cells are full of cell sap (mostly water) which keeps the cell
turgid. The cells pushing against each other provides support.

We will begin with a few definitions.

Habitat	the area where an organism lives
Population	a group of organisms of the same species living in the same area
Community	a group of populations interacting with each other in the same habitat
Environment	the conditions of a certain place
Ecosystem	a community and its environment
Niche	the way in which an organism lives in an ecosystem
Ecology	the study of ecosystems

For example, a pond is an ecosystem consisting of water, the mud at the bottom of it, the plants and all the organisms that live in the pond. The pond community is made up of populations of tadpoles, snails, beetles, plants etc. The habitat of a water snail might be a particular type of pond weed. A tadpole's niche is described by what it eats, its behaviour, what it excretes, and so on.

Sampling

If you are lucky you can count how many of a particular species there are in a certain area. If you want to know how many of a particular plant there are in a field, rather than counting each and every plant (which would take ages and drive you crazy) you take a **sample**. This means that you count how many of a species there are in a small area, and scale it up to get an estimate of how many there are in the whole field (the **abundance**).

Quadrat

This is a square frame. You put it on the ground and count how many of each plant species there are in the square. For plants like grass, where it is difficult to see individual plants, you estimate the percentage of the quadrat that it covers. You do several quadrat samples in random places and take the average.

Transect

This is another way of sampling the distribution of organisms. You place a line across a field (for example) and count all the species that touch the line, or you can count at short intervals – every 10 cm say. Transects are particularly useful to show how the number and kinds of species change as you go from one environment to another, e.g. from a wood to a field.

Estimating populations

Sampling is used to count populations that don't move around much: plants and limpets for example.

To count animals that move around, you can use the **capture, mark, recapture method**. Say you want to count a population of beetles. First you capture a sample (say 40; this will be N_1 in the equation below). You mark each of them in a way that doesn't harm them or make them conspicuous to predators. (A small spot of waterproof paint would work). You release the beetles and then after a suitable period of time, you capture another sample. Hopefully some of these will be marked. The proportion that is marked gives you an indication of the size of the whole population.

$$\text{Population} \approx \frac{\text{Number of animals caught and marked the first time} \times \text{Number of animals caught the second time}}{\text{Number of marked animals caught the second time}}$$

Or, in symbols:

$$P \approx \frac{N_1 \times N_2}{M}$$

For example, if you caught 32 beetles the second time, of which 6 were marked,

$N_1 = 40; N_2 = 32; M = 6;$

therefore, $P = \dfrac{40 \times 32}{6} = 213$

Factors that affect populations

The size of a population is affected by how much food (or nutrients) is available, and how much **competition** there is for it. It is also affected by disease.

Organisms are affected by their environment – the conditions of their habitat. The factors that may affect them include temperature, light, water and the availability of oxygen, carbon dioxide and nutrients. Organisms compete with each other for these factors. Organisms will live where the conditions are most suitable. They are adapted to certain conditions.

A population will grow quickly at first, then the growth slows down and levels off. This happens for many reasons: predators begin to control the growth, the population is affected by diseases, the food supply acts as a limiting factor for further growth, etc. (There is more about factors that affect populations on page 152.)

Energy flow in ecosystems

All energy in ecosystems initially comes from the Sun. Plants use sunlight as energy for photosynthesis to make food and proteins. Animals get their energy from eating plants (herbivores), other animals (carnivores) or both (omnivores).

Food chains

A **food chain** is the sequence in which energy is transferred from organism to organism as food.

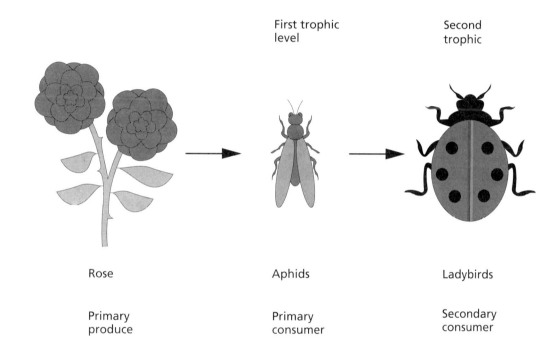

	First trophic level	Second trophic
Rose	Aphids	Ladybirds
Primary produce	Primary consumer	Secondary consumer

A food chain

Green plants are at the beginning of the food chain so they are called **producers**. The animal that eats the plant is the **primary consumer**; it is said to be at the **first trophic level**. (Trophic means feeding.) Any animal that eats that animal is the **secondary consumer** and is said to be at the **second trophic level,** and so on.

Each organism in the chain uses some of the energy for respiration, some is lost as heat, and some is excreted or egested. Also, the whole organism may not be eaten by the next organism in the chain. This means that the amount of energy that is transferred at each step decreases as you go along the chain. All in all, only about 10% of the energy is passed on to the next trophic level.

As the amount of energy at each trophic level decreases, the number of organisms that can be supported decreases. You have to be a bit careful here because if you draw a **pyramid of numbers** (the number of organisms at each trophic level) you don't always get a pyramid (as in the example). If you draw a **pyramid of biomass** (the blocks representing the mass of the organisms at each trophic level) you always get a pyramid that is the right way up.

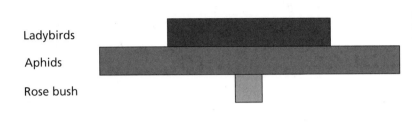

Ladybirds

Aphids

Rose bush

One rose bush provides food for lots of aphids. The size of each level represents the number of organisms feeding at that level.

A pyramid of numbers

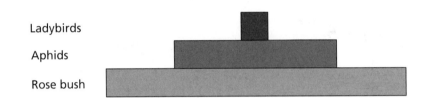

Ladybirds

Aphids

Rose bush

The size of each level represents the mass of the organisms at that level.

A pyramid of biomass

Food chains are usually short, often only three links. Chains are rarely longer than four links because there wouldn't be enough energy to provide another link.

Food webs

Usually there is more than one consumer at each trophic level. Plants are eaten by more than one animal, and animals eat more than one type of plant. This information is put together as a food web, which is really lots of food chains combined. Organisms can also feed at different trophic levels: we are primary consumers when we eat vegetables, but secondary consumers when we eat meat or fish, or drink milk.

Food chains and agriculture

We already know that the amount of energy we get depends on the trophic level we are feeding at – we get more of the initial energy from the Sun when we eat plants than when we eat meat.

This means that an area of land planted with a crop that yields a large amount of energy (e.g. soya beans) can provide food for more people than if the same area of land is used to raise livestock. (This doesn't mean that we would get more energy if we ate grass, rather than the cows or sheep that feed on the grass. The energy in grass is not available to us because we don't have enzymes to digest cellulose – quite a relief really – so in this case it's better to eat the meat.)

Raising of animals always depends on land, even if they are raised intensively, because the cereal that they are fed on has to be grown.

Not all areas of land are suitable for growing crops; hillsides or moorlands for example are better suited to raising animals.

Nutrient cycles

Energy is always lost as you go along the food chain so it has to be constantly fed into an ecosystem. However, nutrients like carbon, oxygen and nitrogen can be **recycled.**

Decomposers like fungi and bacteria are a very important part of ecosystems. They feed on the waste materials and dead bodies of animals and plants. They return nutrients from dead bodies to the ecosystems so that they can be used again.

The carbon cycle

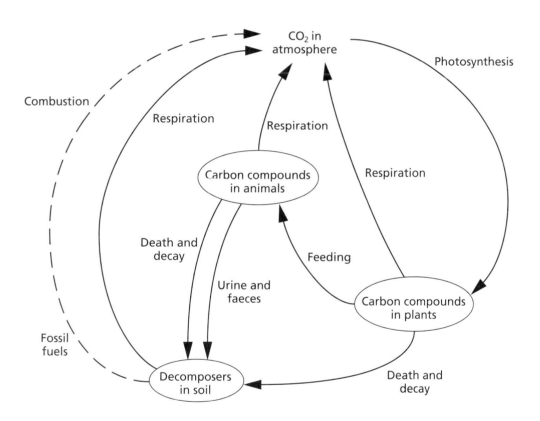

The carbon cycle

Carbon is an essential component of proteins, carbohydrates and fats.

Plants take in carbon in carbon dioxide and use it to make sugars, starch and proteins. Some is used in respiration, so the carbon is released again as carbon dioxide. Animals eat the plants, using some of the glucose for respiration, so the carbon is released again as carbon dioxide. Some of the carbon stays in the animal as proteins, glycogen, glucose, etc. When the plants or animals die, decomposers feed on the bodies. Some of the carbon becomes part of the decomposers' bodies; they release carbon dioxide during respiration; minerals are released into the soil.

Fossil fuels also form part of the carbon cycle. The energy in some decomposing material can become trapped in fossil fuels like oil, gas and coal. When these are burned, carbon dioxide is released.

Burning of an organic material (paper, wood, animal tissues) releases carbon dioxide.

The nitrogen cycle

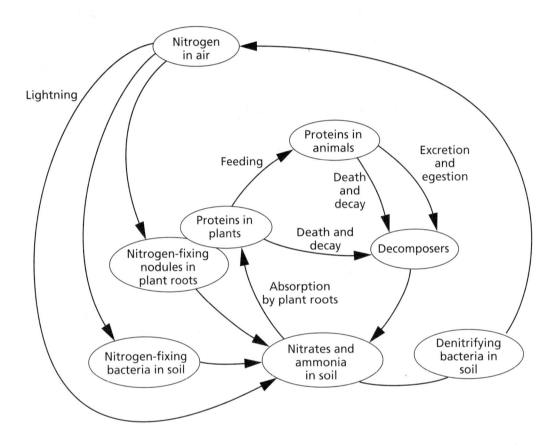

The nitrogen cycle

Nitrogen gas is inert; it makes up 79% of the air and it is breathed in and out without being changed.

To be useful, nitrogen needs to be converted into a more reactive form: **ammonia** (NH_3) or **nitrate** ions (NO_3^-).

This is called **nitrogen fixing**. Bacteria play a big part in this process.

- **Nitrogen-fixing bacteria** combine nitrogen from the air with other substances to form nitrates and other compounds. These bacteria live in the soil or on the root nodules of **leguminous** plants like peas, beans and clover. Farmers rotate their crops so that each field in turn is planted with one of these crops. The roots are left in the ground after the crop is harvested so that nitrogen is available for the next crop.

- **Nitrifying bacteria** turn ammonia into **nitrites** and nitrites into nitrates.

- Decomposers convert protein in dead animals or plants into ammonia. Ploughing plant remains back into the soil to decay therefore improves nitrate levels.

- Nitrogenous waste material from animals (which contains ammonia or urea) is converted to nitrates.

- **Denitrifying bacteria** turn ammonia and nitrates in the soil back into nitrogen, which goes into the atmosphere.

In addition:

- Ammonia and nitrates can be added to soil as fertilisers.

- Lightning is also involved in making nitrates: nitrogen and oxygen in the air combine during lightning to form nitrogen oxides. These dissolve in rain and are washed into the soil where they form nitrates.

- Fixed nitrogen is taken up by plants and used to make amino acids and proteins. Animals eat the plants, taking in nitrogen in the proteins, and use this to make new proteins. This is returned to the system when the animals (or plants) die and decompose.

Worked questions

Q1. *Describe how you would estimate the abundance of dandelions in a garden measuring 10 m by 20 m.*

A1. The population of a plant can be estimated using a quadrat. The quadrat, which measures 1 m^2, is put in a random position in the garden and the number of dandelions in that quadrat is recorded. This is repeated several more times, with the quadrat being placed randomly each time; the more quadrats you count, the more accurate your estimate will be. The mean number of dandelions from all the quadrats is calculated. This gives the number per square metre of garden. The population of dandelions in the whole garden is calculated by multiplying this number by the area of the garden (200 m^2).

Q2. *A group of students decided to estimate the population of snails in a garden using the capture, mark, recapture method. On the first day they caught 75 snails. They marked the snails by painting a spot of yellow enamel paint on the shell and then released them. A week later they caught 66 snails, of which 8 were marked.*

    a) *Estimate the size of the snail population, showing your working.*

    b) *Comment on the suitability of the marker they used and suggest an alternative.*

A2.   a) The population, *P*, of snails is estimated using the following equation:

$$P = \frac{N_1 \times N_2}{M}$$

where N_1 is the number of animals caught and marked the first time, N_2 is the number caught the second time and M is the number of marked animals caught the second time.

$N_1 = 75$; $N_2 = 66$; $M = 8$ so $P = (75 \times 66)/8 = 619$.

b) The yellow enamel paint is not suitable as a marker because it would make the snails conspicuous to predators such as thrushes. Also, the enamel paint would stay on the shell for a long time, rather than being washed off, and it might be toxic to the snail or other species. It is important that markers do not have a detrimental effect on the animal. A better choice of marker would have been green or brown water-soluble paint, which would not be conspicuous and would wash off after a short time.

Q3. *Explain what happens to the energy in a food chain. Why are there no more than three or four levels?*

A3. The base of the food chain is an autotroph i.e. a plant, which obtains its energy from the Sun. The energy is used for biochemical process such as respiration, photosynthesis and building new molecules – proteins and carbohydrates. The primary consumer is a herbivore, which will eat some, but probably not all, of the plant. Some of the plant's energy is used by the herbivore for biochemical processes and for growth; some is lost as heat and in excreted and egested materials. This means that only part of the original energy from the Sun is transferred to the next level of the food chain. The secondary consumer is a carnivore that eats the herbivore. Again, it may not eat all the herbivore. Some of the energy taken in will be used, and some will be lost as heat and through excretion and egestion.

The amount of energy transferred from organism to organism decreases along a food chain. Food chains are rarely longer than three or four links because there wouldn't be enough energy to transfer to support another level.

Q4. *Describe the role of bacteria in the nitrogen cycle.*

A4. Three types of bacteria are involved in the nitrogen cycle, two of which are responsible for converting nitrogen in the air into nitrogen-containing ions that can be used by other organisms. Nitrogen-fixing bacteria live in the soil or on leguminous plants and convert nitrogen into nitrates. Nitrifying bacteria convert ammonia from animal waste and the decomposition of protein in the dead bodies of plants and animals into nitrites, and nitrites into nitrates.

The third type of bacteria involved in the nitrogen cycle are the denitrifying bacteria, which convert ammonia and nitrates in the soil back into nitrogen gas.

topic fourteen

human impact on the environment

Humans affect the environment in many ways.

The ozone layer

They (we) damage the **ozone layer**. This layer of atmosphere (gas) protects us from the harmful **ultraviolet** (UV) radiation from the Sun. UV is short wavelength radiation. When it hits an oxygen molecule, the two oxygen atoms break apart. These are very reactive and react with another oxygen molecule to form ozone – O_3.

$$O_2 \xrightarrow{\text{UV light}} O + O$$

$$O + O_2 \longrightarrow O_3$$

The rate of formation of ozone is usually equal to the rate of breakdown, so there is normally a constant amount of ozone absorbing UV radiation.

The equations for the breakdown of ozone are:

$$O_3 \rightarrow O_2 + O \quad \text{or} \quad O_3 + O \rightarrow 2O_2$$

CFCs damage the ozone layer

Chlorofluorocarbons (CFCs) are the main cause of damage to the ozone layer. CFCs are stable, unreactive, non-toxic chemicals used as coolants, refrigerants and propellants in aerosols. However, if they are released into the atmosphere they gradually reach the ozone layer. (They don't get broken down nearer the ground because they are so stable.) In the ozone layer, the UV radiation breaks the CFC molecules apart, releasing chlorine. Chlorine reacts with ozone so that it breaks down faster than it forms. This means that the amount of ozone in the atmosphere is reduced.

Skin cancer

The ozone layer absorbs UV radiation. This radiation is potentially very dangerous because it can damage DNA and cause **mutations**. Some mutations can lead to **cancer**. **Skin cancer (melanoma)** is the most common type of cancer caused by UV radiation.

Saving the ozone

It is important that we stop using CFCs. Unfortunately, alternative chemicals are expensive, which is no good for developing countries. Also, some of these alternatives might contribute to the **greenhouse effect** (coming up in a minute), which creates a different problem.

Because CFCs are so stable, they will stay in the atmosphere for a long time – including those that are already there. So even if we stop using CFCs immediately, it's still going to take a long time before the amount of ozone gets back to normal.

Global warming and the greenhouse effect

The Earth's atmosphere contains different gases, which help to keep the earth warm. These are the **greenhouse gases**, which include carbon dioxide and **methane**. UV radiation (sunlight) passes through the greenhouse gas layer and reaches and warms the ground. Some is reflected back upwards as long wavelength radiation (called **infrared**) but most cannot get through the layer of greenhouse gases. The radiation reflected back warms the atmosphere.

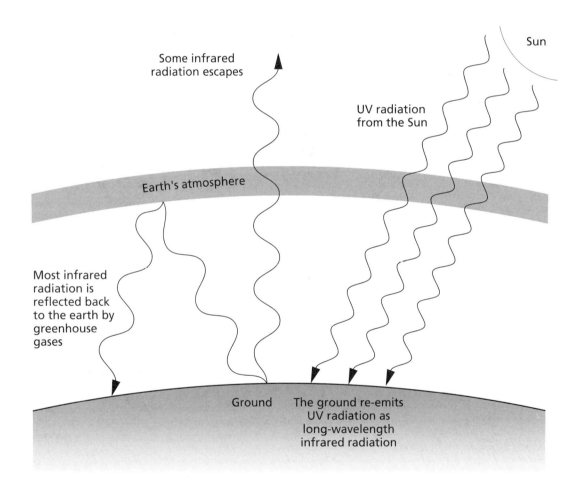

The greenhouse effect

The greenhouse effect heated up the Earth in its early years and kept it warm enough to support life as we know it.

People are now worried that the greenhouse effect is increasing because the amount of carbon dioxide and other greenhouse gases is increasing, trapping more infrared radiation and warming the atmosphere. This might increase the Earth's temperature – **global warming**.

- Carbon dioxide is released into the atmosphere by burning **fossil fuels** (coal, oil, petrol, gas).

- Methane comes from decaying organic matter (waste tips and rice fields), cattle (flatulence) and natural gas leaks.

- Nitrous oxides come from fertilisers and burning fossil fuel.

- CFCs you already know about.

No-one is absolutely sure whether the enhanced greenhouse effect will lead to global warming. If it does, the polar ice caps could melt, leading to disastrous flooding. The weather in different parts of the Earth could change and animals and plants might become extinct.

Can we stop global warming?

Who knows for sure?

- We can certainly cut down the emissions of greenhouse gases by burning less fossil fuel.

- **Deforestation** has been blamed for increasing the amount of carbon dioxide in the air. Burning trees or letting them decay certainly releases large amounts of carbon dioxide into the air, but then there are fewer plants to remove it by photosynthesis.

  It's not always that simple though. Fewer trees would mean that less carbon dioxide is used in photosynthesis. However, fewer trees also means less respiration, and less carbon dioxide going into the atmosphere. Trees that are cut down can be replaced by other plants, which will photosynthesise, removing carbon dioxide.

  Burning trees or letting them decay is the root of the problem.

- We can cut down the amount of nitrous oxide going into the atmosphere by burning less fossil fuel and cutting down on the use of nitrogen-based fertilisers.

- The amount of methane released can be reduced by throwing less rubbish away so that less is decaying in landfill sites. The methane that is produced could be collected and used. Also, rubbish could be burned. This would release carbon dioxide but this doesn't trap as much infrared radiation as the methane would have done.

- CFCs need to be replaced with safer alternatives.

Acid rain

Fossil fuels contain lots of sulphur, and also nitrogen compounds. On burning, **sulphur dioxide** and **nitrogen oxides** are formed.

Sulphur dioxide (SO_2) in itself is an unpleasant gas to breathe in because it irritates your lungs. It can also be poisonous to plants. Sulphur dioxide reacts with water in the atmosphere to form **sulphurous acid** (H_2SO_3), which then reacts with oxygen in the air to form **sulphuric acid** (H_2SO_4). Similar processes happen with the nitrogen oxides, forming **nitric acid**.

Rain is normally weakly acidic because it contains **carbonic acid** (H_2CO_3), a weak acid that forms when carbon dioxide combines with water. The pH is usually about 5.6.

Sulphuric and nitric acids also dissolve in the rain to form **acid rain** which can have a pH as low as 4.

When acid rain seeps into the soil, it washes out important ions like calcium, magnesium and aluminium. Plants become short of these nutrients and die. The ions often end up being washed into rivers and lakes. Aluminium in particular is toxic to fish and other freshwater organisms. Acid rain can also make the water itself more acidic so that animals and plants can't survive.

Reducing acid rain

We can stop acid rain by cutting down the emissions of sulphur dioxide and nitrogen oxides from burning fossil fuels. This is happening as coal-burning power stations are replaced by ones that burn oil.

We can also clean the emissions from power stations. This is called **scrubbing**. The gases are passed through **lime** to remove sulphur dioxide before being released into the atmosphere.

Emissions from burning petrol in cars can be reduced by fitting **catalytic converters**.

Deforestation

Wood is useful for building and as a fuel. Land that has been cleared of trees – **deforestation** – can be used for growing crops.

Rainforests possess an unsurpassed variety of life (**species diversity**). Chopping down the forest destroys the habitat of many rare and wonderful species.

Also, when the trees are chopped down, the soil is exposed to rain. Because the soil layer is very thin, it is easily washed away. This can make it difficult for plants to grow back again. The soil can also end up being washed into river beds, causing flooding.

Nobody is really sure how much effect deforestation has on global warming – unless it is done by burning, which releases lots of carbon dioxide. However, we do know that deforestation can affect the **water cycle**. Rain that falls on trees is taken up and eventually evaporates back into the atmosphere (**transpiration**). If there are no trees, the water falls directly onto the soil and into rivers. This means that less goes back into the air as water vapour so the air is drier and there is less rain.

It is important to conserve rainforests but the people who live in those countries need to be able to grow food. Showing people how to use the rainforest in a *sustainable* way is one answer.

Eutrophication

Fertilisers are used to increase the yield of crops. They usually contain nitrates and phosphates. Nitrates dissolve easily in water and so can be washed out of soil by rain. This is **leaching**.

The nitrates can end up in streams and rivers, which allows **algae** to grow very quickly. This is called an **algal bloom**. It covers the surface of the water, blocking out the light for the plants underneath, which then die. Decomposers feed on the dead material, using up oxygen. This means that there is little oxygen left so other organisms like fish die as well.

This whole process is called **eutrophication**. It can happen whenever food for plants or bacteria is added to water.

Slurry from animal sheds or from pits where grass is rotted down to make **silage** can cause eutrophication. So can sewage, because it produces food for bacteria, which deplete the oxygen as their population grows.

Sometimes, warm water is released into rivers from factories that use water as a coolant. Algae grow more quickly in this warm water than in cold water; also, less oxygen dissolves in water at higher temperature, causing eutrophication. In warm water, organisms that would not normally survive begin to appear, and affect the ecosystem.

Reducing the use of fertilisers

Nitrogen-containing fertilisers can be used carefully so that leaching doesn't occur.

- Apply only as much as the plant can take up straight away.
- Only apply to fields when plants are growing (not to empty fields).
- Do not apply just before rain is forecast.
- Do not spray near streams or rivers.

An alternative is to use **organic** fertilisers such as **manure**. These don't contain many nitrates, and their nutrients are released slowly so that crops can absorb them efficiently. Manures can cause pollution if they are used when crops aren't growing, if a lot is applied at once, or if there is a lot of rain after they are applied.

Crop rotation is also used to maintain soil fertility. This means that different crops are grown in a field each year. Each crop takes different nutrients from the soil, so no one nutrient becomes depleted. (Lack of any one essential nutrient makes a crop fail.) **Legumes** are particularly useful because they *fix* nitrogen, returning it to the soil (see page 120).

Pesticides

Pesticides are used to kill organisms that damage crops. **Insecticides** kill insects; **fungicides** kill fungi; **herbicides** kill weeds (which compete with the crop plant for food, water and light).

Natural ecosystems have a large species diversity, so no one population of species grows too large. In farming, fields often contain only one species (a **monoculture**) or a small number of species. This means that a pest such as an insect or fungus has an unlimited food supply. The population can grow very rapidly, damaging the crop.

The danger of pesticides

Some of the pesticides used in the 1950s and 1960s did a lot of damage to the environment. One of these was the insecticide DDT (dichlorodiphenyltrichloroethane – don't worry about learning the long name!) which had two problems: it was **persistent** and **non-specific**.

Being persistent means that it is not broken down, but stays in the bodies of insects and animals and is passed on to the next trophic level in the food chain (see topic thirteen). This means that DDT **accumulates** and animals at the top of the food chain get a large concentration of DDT.

Because DDT is non-specific, it doesn't just kill insects; it is also harmful to other animals and birds. The dosage of DDT that is enough to kill insects accumulates through the food chain and is enough to kill or harm other animals higher up the food chain. DDT is now banned in Britain but is still used in some developing countries.

Reducing the use of pesticides

Pesticides are expensive and take time to apply, as well as causing other problems. Reducing their use is therefore a good idea.

One way is to use pesticides only when they are actually needed, rather than 'just in case'. Researchers have found ways of predicting when there will be high levels of some pests (because of weather conditions, time of year, etc.) and can tell farmers when to use the pesticides.

Biological control

Biological control means using a natural predator or parasite to keep the number of pests under control. This is called the **control organism**. An obvious example is having cats in a farmyard to catch rats and mice. Another example is the greenhouse whitefly which can be controlled by introducing a small wasp called *Encarsia formosa* into the greenhouse. Wasp larvae live and feed inside whitefly larvae, killing them.

Biological control is usually **specific** – it only affects the pest, not useful insects like bees. It is cheaper than pesticides, and pests don't become **resistant** to the control organism. (Resistance means that the pest is no longer killed by the pesticide.)

... out of control

Sometimes biological control can get out of control. **Cane toads** were introduced in Australia to control beetles that were destroying sugar cane crops. The toad did its job very well, but bred rapidly. There are now so many that native amphibians have been driven out. The toad also eats other native animals, and it secretes a poison on its skin that can kill other animals.

It is therefore important that biological controls will not affect the natural ecosystem.

Worked questions

Q1. *Describe the effect of chlorofluorocarbons (CFCs) on the ozone layer. Why are people so worried about the effects of CFCs?*

A1. Chlorofluorocarbons (CFCs) damage the ozone layer which protects the Earth from ultraviolet (UV) radiation. CFCs are stable at ground level, but are broken down in the atmosphere to release chlorine. The chlorine reacts with ozone so that the ozone breaks down faster than it is formed. This means that the amount of ozone is decreasing, so the amount of harmful UV radiation reaching the Earth is increasing. The UV radiation can cause skin cancer. Also, CFCs act as greenhouse gases, which trap infrared radiation between the earth and the atmosphere; this is thought to contribute to global warning.

Q2. *Name three greenhouse gases and explain where they come from.*

A2. Three greenhouses gases are:
   i)   carbon dioxide which is released by the burning of fossil fuels
   ii) methane which is released from cattle (flatulence) and decaying organic matter (waste tips and paddy fields)
   iii) nitrous oxides, which come from fertilisers and burning fossil fuel.

   (You could also include CFCs here, but the question only asked for three examples.)

Q3. *DDT is a pesticide that is both non-specific and persistent. Explain the meaning of the terms a) pesticide, b) non-specific, and c) persistent.*

A3. a) A pesticide is a chemical that is used to kill unwanted organisms.
   b) Non-specific means that the pesticide doesn't just kill the pest it is targeted at. DDT was used as an insecticide but also killed animals higher up the food chain.
   c) Persistent means that the DDT is not broken down. Birds ate the insects that had been sprayed with DDT and the DDT accumulated in the birds' bodies, eventually poisoning them.

Q4. *a) What is meant by a biological control? Give an example.*
   b) Give an example of an attempt at biological control that was not entirely successful, explaining what went wrong.

A4. a) Biological control means using a natural predator or parasite to control the population of a pest. For example, a wasp called *Encarsia formosa* is used to control whitefly in greenhouses. The wasp lives and feeds in the whitefly larvae, thereby killing the pest.
   b) The cane toad was introduced in Australia to control beetles that were destroying the sugar cane crops, which it did very successfully. However, it was so successful that it became established and reproduced. It drove out native amphibians, ate other native species and a substance in its skin poisoned would-be predators. It therefore completely destroyed the natural ecosystem.

genetics

Genetics is the part of biology that tells us about why we are the way we are. It tells us why we have inherited certain characteristics from our parents (some of which we may be grateful for, and some of which we aren't).

Chromosomes

The **nuclei** of cells contain chromosomes – long strings of **DNA**, bound by protein.

Different species have different numbers of chromosomes. Humans have 46 in each cell, donkeys have 64. Every cell in each organism in the same species has the same number of chromosomes (except the gametes of course which have half the number).

Chromosomes exist in homologous pairs, as was explained in topic nine. One chromosome in the pair comes from each parent. Each chromosome has two **chromatids**, so there are four chromatids in each pair of homologous chromosomes – this is important for reasons we'll see in a minute.

Genes

A **gene** is a strand of DNA. It is responsible for a particular characteristic of an organism. It is copied and passed on to the next generation. Genes control characteristics by making proteins; a gene is the chemical code (or set of instructions) to make a particular protein. Different genes provide the codes for different proteins; different proteins cause different characteristics. The protein could be structural (e.g. muscle) or it could be an enzyme that controls a particular metabolic reaction.

Each cell in your body has a complete copy of all your genes. However, not all the genes are 'switched on' in each cell. For example, all the cells in your body have the gene that makes **keratin**, the protein in hair. This gene is switched on in the cells on your scalp, so keratin is produced. The cells in your stomach also contain this gene but it is not switched on, so keratin is not made here. Similarly, the genes that control hair colour are only switched on in cells that are instructed to make hair.

Alleles

Each gene is in the same position in each chromosome of a homologous pair. The gene can have different forms. These forms are called **alleles**.

Alleles   different forms of the same gene

During meiosis, each of the four chromatids in a homologous pair of chromosomes ends up in a different daughter cell, so each daughter cell ends up with one allele of a gene.

After fertilisation, the zygote has two alleles, one from each parent. A combination of these two alleles determines the characteristic that is **expressed**. (Keep reading to find out what this means.)

Genotype and phenotype

- The combination of alleles is the genetic make-up, or **genotype**.

- The way the alleles are expressed is the **phenotype**.

Alleles can be **dominant** or **recessive**. Both copies of a recessive allele need to be present in the cell for their characteristic to be expressed, i.e. appear in the individual.

For example, the allele causing brown eye colour is dominant to the allele causing blue eye colour; the blue colour allele is recessive. Two alleles are present. If both are the brown allele, then the eyes will be brown. If both are the blue allele, the eyes will be blue. If one is the brown allele, and the other is the blue allele, then the dominance comes into play. Brown is dominant, so the eyes will be brown.

A dominant allele is given a capital letter. In the case above, it could be B, for brown. A recessive allele is given a lower case letter. In the case above, it could be b for blue (technically the b means 'not brown').

> *(The same letter is used for each allele, so if the dominant allele were red and the recessive allele were white, R and r would be used. [This might seem like a stupid example, but some insects have red eyes.]*
>
> *Try to use letters that are different in upper and lower case; try not to use things like W and w.)*

The genotype can take three forms.

BB   Both the alleles are the same, so the genotype is **homozygous dominant**. The phenotype is brown eye colour.

bb   Both the alleles are the same, so the genotype is **homozygous recessive**. The phenotype is blue eye colour.

Bb   The alleles are different, so the genotype is **heterozygous**. The phenotype is brown eye colour, as B is dominant to b.

The recessive alleles only have effect if the genotype is homozygous recessive.

Cystic fibrosis

People with cystic fibrosis make too much mucus in their lungs. The mucus is thicker than normal and collects in the lungs, making gaseous exchange difficult and providing a breeding ground for bacteria.

The thick mucus is also made in the pancreas. It blocks the pancreatic duct, stopping digestive enzymes from flowing into the duodenum.

The mucus is made partly by a protein in the cell membrane. This protein is made incorrectly in people with cystic fibrosis.

There are two alleles for the gene that makes this protein. The dominant allele (F) makes a normal protein; the recessive allele (f) makes the incorrect protein. There are three genotypes.

Genotype		Phenotype
FF	Homozygous dominant	This person will not have cystic fibrosis. His or her gametes will always contain an F allele.
Ff	Heterozygous	This person will not have cystic fibrosis. However, he or she is a **carrier** because the f allele could be passed on to the next generation in the gametes.
ff	Homozygous recessive	This person will have cystic fibrosis. His or her gametes will always contain an f allele.

You can predict the proportion of the different genotypes in the offspring using a **genetic cross**.

Genetic cross for cystic fibrosis

(It's important that you write out genetic crosses clearly and use the right symbols – otherwise it gets confusing. Always say what letter you are going to use for the two alleles.)

Phenotypes of parents	Normal (carrier)	x	Cystic fibrosis
Genotypes of parents	Ff	x	ff
Gametes	Ⓕ or Ⓕ	x	Ⓕ

We then use a diagram called a **Punnett square** to work out the genotypes of the first generation, which is called the F1 generation. (F stands for filial here.) The next generation from crossing two F1 offspring is called the F2 generation.

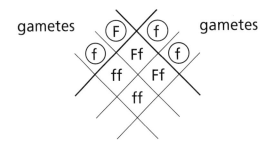

The letters in the diamonds represent the possible genotypes of the offspring.

The **ratio** of genotypes in the offspring is 2Ff : 2ff.

The ratio of phenotypes in the offspring is therefore 2 normal : 2 cystic fibrosis, or 1 : 1.

So, in theory, half the offspring will be normal, but carriers, and half will have cystic fibrosis. Remember, though, that this is only an estimate; a **probability**. This means that each child that is born has a 1 in 2 chance of having cystic fibrosis. If the first child is born with cystic fibrosis, this doesn't mean that the next child will be a carrier; the chance is still 1 in 2.

Muscular dystrophy is another example of an inherited condition that is caused by a recessive gene.

You can also work out what would happen if both parents are carriers.

Phenotypes of parents	Normal (carrier)	x	Normal (carrier)
Genotypes of parents	Ff	x	Ff
Gametes	(F) or (f)	x	(F) or (f)

F1 generation

gametes (F) X (F) gametes

(f) X FF X (f)

Ff X Ff

ff

The ratio of genotypes will be 1 FF : 2 Ff : 1 ff. This means that there is a 1 in 4 chance that a child will have cystic fibrosis and a 1 in 2 (2 in 4) chance that the child will be a carrier. Couples who know that they are both carriers of the cystic fibrosis genes can therefore work out the chance that a child they have will have the illness. If only one of the couple is a carrier but the other is normal (FF), none of their children will have cystic fibrosis (because they will always inherit at least one dominant gene), although some will be carriers. (Check this by doing a Punnett square.)

Codominance

Not all alleles are decisively dominant or recessive.

Codominance   both alleles affect the phenotypes

The alleles are shown as a capital C with a superscript letter for the allele. Snapdragons are a common example of codominance.

The C^R allele produces a red colour.

The C^W allele produces a white colour.

Genotype	Phenotype
$C^R C^R$	Red flowers
$C^W C^W$	White flowers
$C^R C^W$	Pink flowers – both the red and the white alleles have an effect

Incomplete dominance

This is somewhere between complete dominance (as in cystic fibrosis genes) and codominance (as in the snapdragon genes). The extent of effect of the alleles is different.

An example is **sickle cell anaemia**. People with sickle cell anaemia produce an abnormal type of haemoglobin which doesn't carry oxygen as well as normal haemoglobin. At low oxygen concentrations (e.g. during exercise) the abnormal haemoglobin forms a precipitate in the red blood cells and they become curved and sickle shaped. These cells get stuck in capillaries, stopping oxygen supply to muscles and causing pain.

The allele for the abnormal haemoglobin, h, is recessive; the allele for normal haemoglobin, H, is dominant.

Genotype	Phenotype
HH	Normal
hh	Sickle cell anaemia
Hh	Mild sickle cell anaemia

People who have the hh genotype often die before they have children. People with the Hh genotype are more resistant to **malaria** than those with the HH genotype. People with the HH phenotype do not die from sickle cell anaemia, but may die from malaria. This means that the heterozygous genotype Hh is more common than you might predict.

Sex chromosomes

Each person has two **sex chromosomes**. The other 44 chromosomes are called **autosomes**.

There are two different sex chromosomes: the X chromosome looks like the letter X; the Y chromosome looks like the letter Y and is shorter than the X chromosome.

The sex chromosomes determine what sex you are: women have two X chromosomes; men have an X and a Y chromosome. You can say that their genotypes are XX and XY, respectively, although the letters apply to a whole chromosome rather than a single gene.

Female gametes (eggs) always contain an X chromosome; male gametes (sperm) can contain either an X or a Y chromosome.

You can work out how sex is inherited using a genetic cross, just as for other genes. Don't forget that the letters represent whole chromosomes.

Phenotypes of parents	Male	Female
Genotypes of parents	XY	XX
Gametes	Ⓧ or Ⓨ	Ⓧ
Offspring		

male
gametes
Ⓧ Ⓧ
Ⓨ XX
XY
female
gametes

So, half the children will be boys, and half will be girls (in theory). What this really means is that there is a 1 in 2 chance that a child will be a boy and a 1 in 2 chance that it will be a girl.

Sex-linked genes

The sex chromosomes carry genes, just like the autosomes. However, the X and Y chromosomes are not a homologous pair and they don't necessarily carry the same genes.

Some genes are **sex linked**. This means that they are carried on only one of the sex chromosomes – usually the X chromosome. The Y chromosome may not have the matching gene.

Haemophilia is an example of a sex-linked disease. The dominant allele, H, allows the blood to clot normally. The recessive allele, h, means that the blood doesn't clot properly. The gene is on the X chromosome, but not on the Y chromosome because it is carried on the **non-homologous** part of the chromosome. There are three possible genotypes in women, but only two in men.

	Genotype	Phenotype
Women	$X^H X^H$	Normal
	$X^H X^h$	Normal; carrier
	$X^h X^h$	Haemophilia
Men	$X^H Y$	Normal
	$X^h Y$	Haemophilia

A woman who is heterozygous for the haemophilia gene is said to be a carrier because she can pass the gene to her children, just as happens with the cystic fibrosis gene.

Phenotype of parents	Normal man	Carrier woman
Genotype of parents	$X^H Y$	$X^H X^h$
Gametes	X^H or Y	X^H or X^h
Offspring		

$X^H X^H$	Normal female
$X^H X^h$	Carrier female
$X^H Y$	Normal male
$X^h Y$	Male with haemophilia

This means that there is a 1 in 2 chance that a male child will have haemophilia.

Red–green colour blindness is another example of a sex-linked **trait**. The colour-blindness gene is on the X chromosome.

Selective breeding

This basically means that you decide which of a population of animals or plants you breed from so that a particular trait is passed on. This trait could be yield, flavour, disease resistance, etc. in plants, or coat colour, size, temperament, etc. in animals. With plants, pollen can be physically transferred from one plant to another; with animals, **artificial insemination** can be used.

If this process is repeated for several generations you will eventually get a **pure-breeding** strain in which the offspring are always identical to the parents for a particular trait. All the individuals are homozygous for that trait.

Selective breeding has produced main-crop plants that are high yield, drought resistant, disease resistant or that grow quickly. Many **pedigree** dogs or cats are bred in this way.

Inbreeding is when you cross two close relatives. If you do this too much, the offspring become less healthy and show defects. Some pedigree dogs are highly inbred and have many health problems. This happens because many recessive genes are homozygous and are therefore expressed. A disadvantage of inbred plants can be that, because they are all so similar, an infection or pest could kill all of them, instead of just the weaker ones.

Outbreeding means crossing two unrelated individuals to make a **hybrid**. This process usually produces strong healthy individuals – **hybrid vigour**.

Plant propagation

Gardeners and farmers can produce fresh stocks of plants that are identical to the parent by taking **shoot cuttings**. This is called **vegetative (asexual) reproduction** and the new plants are **clones** of the parent because they are genetically identical.

The stem is cut just below the point where a leaf joins the stem (a **node**); most of the leaves are stripped away – new shoots grow where the old leaves were taken off. Roots will grow from the cut end of the shoot (these are **adventitious roots**).

Another method is **grafting**. A twig from one plant is placed in a slit in the stem of a tree or bush that has already rooted well. The tissues of the twig (the **scion**) and the tree (the **stock**) join together and the **graft** grows on the stock.

Micropropagation

Many kinds of plants can be grown from small pieces using tissue culture. The liquid or jelly (**agar**) that they are grown in provides all the nutrients etc., and conditions are **sterile** so the new plants are free of disease. All the plants will be clones of the parent plant. Commercially important plants like the oil palm can be produced in large numbers using this method. You can make the clones from a plant that produces a lot of oil, so that all the new plants are just as productive.

(Go back to page 85 to remind yourself of the pros and cons of sexual and asexual reproduction.)

Protein synthesis from DNA

DNA (deoxyribonucleic acid) carries the instructions for proteins to be made (genes are made of DNA). It is made of two strands twisted together – a **double helix**. The strands are held together by **bases** which always pair up in the same way:

- **adenine** (A) pairs with **thymine** (T)

- **cytosine** (C) pairs with **guanine** (G).

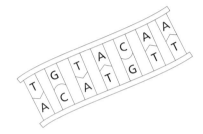

a) A strand of DNA is made up of pairs of bases.

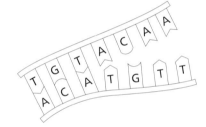

b) The two strands of DNA separate.

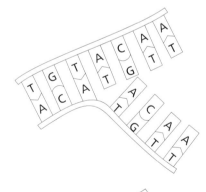

c) New bases are added to each strand. Remember that A always pairs with T; C always pairs with G.

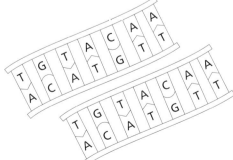

d) Two new strands of DNA are formed, each is identical to the original strand. The strands form a new double helix.

This shows the process of DNA replication during mitosis. (Messenger RNA [mRNA] for protein synthesis is formed in a similar way but the mRNA comes away from the DNA and goes off to the ribosome, and the DNA zips back together.)

When proteins are made, the DNA unravels and the two strands separate (like undoing a zip). A template of the DNA is made using **messenger RNA** (this process is called **transcription**) which then takes the instructions to the **ribosomes** on the **endoplasmic reticulum**, which is where proteins are made (in the process of **translation**).

The sequence of bases makes the code for the new protein. The bases are arranged in sets of three (**triplets**); each set is the code for a particular amino acid. (You can think of the bases as letters, the triplets as words, and the whole strand of DNA as a very long sentence.) The sequence CAG is the code for the amino acid **valine** so the sequence CAGCAGCAG means three valines in a row. Each amino acid is carried to the ribosome by a tRNA (**transfer** RNA) molecule which has the right triplet. In this way strings of amino acids are linked together to make proteins.

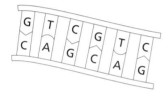

a) The DNA contains sets of three bases (triplets).

b) The mRNA is copied from the DNA strand and goes off to a ribosome.

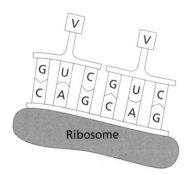

c) Molecules of tRNA carrying the amino acid (valine in this case) and the correct triplet join with the mRNA. The two valine molecules are then joined together.

*Making proteins from DNA. (The base in RNA that pairs with T is **uracil** [U].)*

Mutations

DNA is copied during meiosis and mitosis. The DNA 'unzips' as it does during protein synthesis, but a new strand of DNA is formed. Usually the sequence of bases is copied very exactly. Occasionally though a base is changed or moved out of sequence. This is called a **mutation**.

This can change the protein molecule that is produced, which may affect the phenotype. For example, a mutation can cause an **albino** baby to be born to a family with dark skin; the protein that produces the skin colour is affected.

Radiation can cause mutations in the DNA. If this happens in the testes or ovaries, the altered DNA can be passed on to the offspring.

Chromosome changes

Sometimes homologous chromosomes don't separate properly during meiosis, and both chromosomes go into one daughter cell instead of one into each. This is what happens in **Down's Syndrome**. Some eggs receive both copies of chromosome 21. If the egg is fertilised, the zygote has three copies of chromosome 21, as does every cell as the zygote grows. This causes Down's Syndrome.

Worked questions

Q1. Define the following terms:

a) heterozygous

b) phenotype

A1. a) A heterozygous organism has two different alleles of a particular gene.

b) This is the way in which the genotype is expressed.

Q2. Give an example of an autosomal recessive disease, and describe its symptoms.

A2. Cystic fibrosis is an example of an autosomal recessive disease. The gene makes a protein that is involved in production of mucus in the lungs. In people with cystic fibrosis, there is too much mucus and it is thicker than normal. The mucus collects in the lungs making gaseous exchange difficult, and traps bacteria.

The thick mucus is also made in the pancreas where it blocks the pancreatic duct and stops pancreatic juice, which contains digestive enzymes, from flowing into the duodenum.

Q3. What is meant by codominance? Use an example to illustrate your answer. How is codominance represented in a genetic cross?

A3. Codominance occurs when alleles are not completely dominant or recessive and both have an effect on the phenotype. Petal colour in flowers is a typical example: when an organism has a red-petal allele and a white-petal allele, the petals are pink.

Codominance is shown as a capital C (for codominance) and superscript letters for the alleles, for example C^R and C^W combine to form $C^R C^W$ (pink petals).

Q4. Haemophilia is an X-linked recessive disorder. If a normal male mates with a carrier female, what is the probability that:

a) a female child will be haemophiliac?

b) a given child will be haemophiliac?

c) a given child will be a carrier for the disease?

A4. H is used to represent the dominant gene; h for the recessive gene.

Phenotype of parents	Normal male	Carrier female
Genotype of parents	X^HY	X^HX^h
Gametes	X^H or Y	X^H or X^h

Offspring

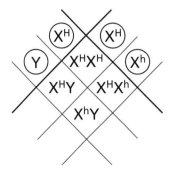

X^HX^H Normal female
X^HX^h Carrier female
X^HY Normal male
X^hY Male with haemophilia

a) 0

b) 1 in 4

c) 1 in 4

[You could argue that males with cystic fibrosis (X^hY) are also carriers, so the probability is 2 in 4, or 1 in 2.]

Life on Earth began 4000 million years ago, with very simple organisms. Since then, organisms have gradually changed. There are more different organisms and they have become more complex. They have also become **adapted** to their surroundings. This is the process of **evolution**. This process is still going on. Humans have only been around for about 4 million years whereas protoctists have been around for about 1200 million years. (So really we aren't as important as we think we are.)

Clues about evolution

Fossils

Fossils give us some clues about the types of animal that were around millions of years ago. Fossils are the remains or impression of an organism preserved in rock. Dead organisms buried in silt decompose and dissolve, leaving a space in the silt (a bit like a mould). Minerals seep into the space and solidify in the shape of the organism, and the silt solidifies into rock so that the fossil becomes embedded in the rock.

You can get some idea of the age of a fossil from the age of the rock that it is embedded in. Fossils from 3000 million years ago are very simple organisms like bacteria, whereas the ones from 'younger' rocks are more complex organisms. Sometimes quite large skeletons have been found, like dinosaurs or a fossilised whale.

Fossils are quite difficult to find because their formation was rare. This means that the fossil record is incomplete and we do not have a very clear idea of all the organisms that lived in the past and how they gradually changed.

Homologous and vestigial structures

If you look at the human arm, it is made up of a single upper arm bone (the humerus) connected to two foream bones (the ulna and radius) by a hinged joint (the elbow). The wrist is a gliding joint which connects to the small wrist bones, which are connected to the hand and finger bones. The way the bones in the hand are arranged means that we can grasp things and manipulate objects. The arm is flexible but very strong.

Birds have almost the same arrangement of bones in their wings, but the shapes of the bones are different so that they are suitable for flying. Bats also have a similar structure, but the finger bones are very long and thin to form the wings. Even whales have a similar structure in their fins, but the shape of the bones is adapted for swimming.

The limbs all have the same basic design, but have become adapted for different purposes. Structures like this are called **homologous structures**. It seems unlikely that it is a coincidence that all these animals developed the same basic design. Scientists think that the different animals have evolved from a **common ancestor**.

Some animals have **vestigial** structures. These are 'leftover' structures that the animal doesn't need any more. For example, pythons have small limb bones. Snakes have probably evolved from lizards and, because they don't need limbs for walking, these have gradually got smaller over millions of years. In fact, some snakes don't have any at all.

Darwin and natural selection

Charles Darwin published a book in 1859 called *The Origin of Species* in which he suggested how evolution could have happened – the theory of **natural selection**. His theory goes like this.

- Rather than all being identical, individual organisms in a population vary slightly from each other. This **variation** (more about this in a minute) means that some individuals are better *adapted* to their environment than others.

- Organisms produce more young than are likely to survive to be adults (**over production**) but the population usually stays stable.

- There is competition between individuals for things like food that they need to survive (the **struggle for existence**).

- The ones that are best adapted are most likely to survive, for example those that can run fastest so they are not caught by predators (or can catch their prey, depending on the type of animal); those that are tallest so they can reach more food; those that are most resistant to disease. For plants it might be those with the longest roots to reach water, or with seeds that are best adapted for dispersal. This is called **survival of the fittest**.

- The well-adapted organisms breed so the advantageous characteristics are passed on to their offspring.

- The poorly adapted individuals do not survive to breed so *gradually*, the population of organisms becomes adapted to its environment. If the environment in which the animals live changes in some way, the whole process starts again.

Natural selection means that genotypes which produce phenotypes that are beneficial for survival are passed on to the next generation.

Natural selection helps organisms to adapt to *changes* in their environment. If the environment stays stable, populations stay much the same from one generation to the next because the organisms are well adapted. This is called **stabilising selection**. For example, **coelacanths** live deep in the Indian ocean, which is a very stable environment. They haven't changed much in more than 350 million years.

If organisms do not adapt quickly enough to changes in their environment, they can become extinct (as happened to dinosaurs). Many animals are in danger of becoming extinct because humans are destroying their habitats.

Variation

Discontinuous variation is where individuals fit into one of two definite categories for a particular characteristic. For example, you either can or can't roll your tongue; there is no in-between category.

Continuous variation is really the opposite: there are no definite categories. Height is an example of continuous variation: there are lots of different heights. If you record how many people are of particular heights, you should get a **normal distribution curve**. Most people are in the middle of the range and a few are very tall or very short.

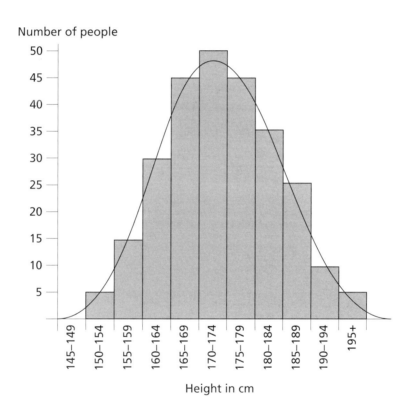

This graph shows a normal distribution curve for the heights of a group of people. The bars show how many people are in each range of heights: 25 people were 185–189 cm tall.

Genes are the basis of variation. Genes control **traits** that show discontinuous variation. For example, whether or not you can roll your tongue is controlled by a gene. Genes are also involved in traits that show continuous variation, like height, weight, hair colour, etc. but **environmental factors** are also involved. For example, a tree's genes determine how tall it *could* grow, but the environment – how much water, light, nutrients, space etc. it has – will determine how tall it actually gets.

Characteristics that are not genetic, but are caused by the organism's environment, are called **acquired characteristics**. They are not passed on to the next generation because they are not caused by genes. For example, a plant may have only small fruit because of lack of nutrients. This acquired characteristic will not be passed on. It may have a gene for particularly large fruit (if conditions are right). This gene would be passed on.

Two organisms that are genetically identical may appear different if they are raised in different environments.

Variation arises in several ways.

- During **meiosis**, genes are exchanged between **homologous chromosomes** so that the four **gametes** formed are not genetically identical.

- At **fertilisation**, two gametes fuse together, so lots of different combinations of genes can be produced in the **zygote**. If, like humans, the organism has lots of different genes, it is highly unlikely that two offspring will have the same **genotype** (although they might for one particular characteristic). This is why brothers and sisters can be alike in some ways but not in others (which is probably a relief for everyone).

- **Mutations** (see page 138) can cause changes in a gene. Sometimes these changes are harmful (as in sickle cell anaemia), and sometimes they are beneficial. If a mutation is beneficial, it might improve the organism's chance of survival, so that the mutation is passed on to its offspring.

Evolution in action

Although on a grand scale, evolution has happened over millions of years, natural selection is a continuous process.

Peppered moths

The peppered moth has black-and-white speckled wings that provide camouflage for resting on lichen-covered tree trunks. The black colour (or **melanic** form) is caused by a single dominant gene. This means that some moths will be more black than white. The black moths are less well camouflaged than the speckled moths so they are more likely to be eaten by birds. This means that they are less likely to survive to produce offspring.

During the industrial revolution, the environment of these moths living near large cities changed: pollution stopped the lichen growing on the tree trunks. This meant that the black moths were better camouflaged than the speckled ones. They were less likely to be eaten by birds and so they survived and passed this characteristic on to their offspring. Dark moths were therefore **selected** for survival. Being eaten (predation) by birds is the **selection pressure** because that is the factor that decided which ones survived.

In rural (i.e. unpolluted) areas where the lichen grows on trees, the speckled moths still have the selective advantage over the black moths.

Antibiotic resistance

Some bacteria develop mutations which mean that they are not killed by antibiotics like penicillin. If you take penicillin, the **resistant** bacteria are provided with a huge selective advantage because they can go on reproducing while all the other bacteria are killed. This means that the number of resistant bacteria increases massively, and penicillin no longer works.

The more you use antibiotics, the more likely this is to happen. **'Superbugs'** are bacteria that are resistant to virtually every antibiotic, which means that they are very difficult to kill. You shouldn't take antibiotics unless you really have to, to minimise the number of resistant bacteria.

Sickle cell anaemia

We discussed sickle cell anaemia in topic fifteen. People who are heterozygous are resistant to malaria, which means that they have a strong selective advantage in areas where there is malaria. (People who are homozygous recessive for the sickle cell gene die of sickle cell anaemia, often before they have children; homozygous dominants are more likely to die of malaria, possibly before they have children.)

If two heterozygotes have children, some are likely to be homozygotes; this is why sickle cell anaemia hasn't died out even though people who have it don't usually survive. This selective advantage only works in areas where there is malaria (malaria is the selection pressure). In areas where there is no malaria, there is no selective advantage for the recessive allele and it is gradually lost from the population.

Artificial selection

Artificial selection (selective breeding; see page 136) is really the manmade version of natural selection because we decide which phenotype we want to be passed on to the next generation of animals or plants, rather than the one that necessarily provides the best adaptation to the environment.

Worked questions

Q1.   What are fossils? Why is the fossil record incomplete?

A1.   Fossils are organisms or imprints of organisms that have become embedded and preserved in rock. The age of the rock gives you an idea of how old the fossilised organism is.

Only a few organisms that die actually form fossils, so fossils are quite rare and are difficult to find. This is why the fossil record is incomplete.

Q2.   Explain what is meant by 'survival of the fittest'.

A2.   Survival of the fittest is part of Darwin's theory of natural selection. Organisms within a population show variation in different traits, which might affect their ability to survive. The organisms that are best adapted survive – survival of the fittest – and pass their beneficial traits on to their offspring.

Q3. *What is the difference between continuous and discontinuous variation? Give an example of each to illustrate your answer.*

A3. Discontinuous variation describes a trait that is obviously divided into two categories. For example, you can either roll your tongue or you can't; there is no in-between category.

Continuous variation describes a trait for which there are lots of possible categories. Height and weight are examples. Discontinuous traits are determined by genes; continuous traits are determined by genes and environmental factors.

Q4. *What is artificial selection? Give an example to illustrate your answer.*

A4. In artificial selection, you choose which animal or plant you want to breed from so that a particular trait is passed on to the offspring. This is used in developing new strains of crops. For example, if wheat is found to be resistant to a predator or disease, the seed from the wheat is used for the next generation. This is repeated for several generations until eventually all the offspring show the desirable trait.

the diversity of life

There are millions and millions of different types of organisms in the world. For example, there are over a million different species of insect, and those are just the ones we know about!

Classification of organisms

Organisms can be classified into groups according to how they are related to one another. These groups are called **homologies** and the system is called **binomial classification**. (The idea was dreamt up by a Swedish naturalist called Linnaeus, long before Darwin was around; he didn't know about evolution and didn't realise that animals that are similar are related.) The classification system is shown in the diagram.

Species are the basic unit of classification. Animals only breed with members of the same species. Dogs all belong to the same species, but there are many different breeds, all of which are obviously dogs. Different breeds of dog can mate to produce mongrels.

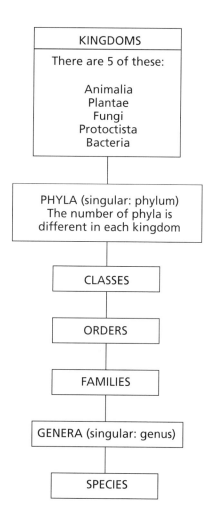

The order of classification

Naming species

Species are named in Latin according to their **genus** and species. (Binomial means two names.) Different people may use different local names for a plant, for example, but its Latin name is always the same.

To name an organism, write its genus (**generic** name) first, starting with a capital letter, and then its species (**specific** name), which does not start with a capital letter. The Latin name is in italics if it is printed; underline the name when it is hand written. For example, the stoat and weasel are members of the same genus. The stoat is *Mustela erminea*; the weasel is *Mustela nivalis*. Although it may not always seem like it, the names are logical and usually describe the organism in some way.

The five kingdoms

Bacteria

This kingdom (sometimes called **monera**) includes **bacteria** and **blue–green algae**. The organisms are **unicellular** (single-celled) have a cell wall, but do not have a nucleus. Bacteria reproduce by repeatedly splitting into two to form colonies. (These are seen as plaques on agar plates, or cloudiness in solution.)

Viruses are smaller than bacteria but they are non-living (i.e. they are not complete cells). They consist of a packet of genetic material surrounded by a protective coat. Viruses reproduce by infecting cells in the body. The cell's machinery is used to replicate the genetic material. The cell is then lysed so that the newly made viruses are released.

Protoctista

These are simple organisms, some are unicellular and some are **multicellular** (e.g. seaweed). They have nuclei (i.e. the chromosomes are enclosed in a nuclear membrane). They nearly all live in water. Some are animal-like, feeding on other living things (*Amoeba* is an example). Others are plant-like and photosynthesise; these have chloroplasts containing chlorophyll (or a similar type of pigment).

Fungi

Fungi include toadstools, mushrooms, moulds and things like puffballs. Yeasts are single-celled fungi.

Fungi are mostly multicellular organisms. They are made up of chains of cells called **hyphae** which grow out in all directions, eventually forming a **mycelium**. The hyphae secrete enzymes which digest the food material. The cells have cell walls and nuclei, which are distributed throughout the cytoplasm in the hyphae.

Fungi feed parasitically (see page 161) or saprophytically (see page 31); they do not photosynthesise (they do not have chlorophyll). When fungi need to move to another food source, the hyphae grow upwards and form branches. The tips of the branches release **spores**, which are carried away by physical contact and by air currents to new locations.

Plantae

Organisms in the plantae kingdom are multicellular. Their cells have cell walls and nuclei. The organisms feed by photosynthesis and so they usually have chlorophyll (or a similar pigment). There are four phyla: mosses and liverworts (**bryophytes**); ferns (**filicinophytes**); conifers (**coniferophytes**); flowering plants (**angiospermophytes**). We need to know the basic features of each phlyum.

Bryophtes	Filicinophytes	Coniferophytes	Angiospermophytes
Mosses and liverworts	*Ferns*	*Conifers (trees or shrubs)*	*Flowering plants*
• Simple stems and leaves	• Roots, stems and leaves	• Roots, stems and leaves	• Roots, stems and leaves
• No phloem or xylem	• Stem is below ground (**rhizome**)	• Needle-like leaves	• Xylem and phloem
• Live in water	• Xylem and phloem	• Xylem and phloem	• Insect or wind pollinated
• Single-celled **rhizoids** act as roots	• Young 'leaves' are coiled and unwind	• Pollen containing male gametes carried by wind	• Reproduce by seeds which grow inside fruits developed from the flower's ovaries
• Reproduce sexually	• Reproduce by spore held in spore bodies called **sporangia**	• Reproduce by seeds which develop in cones	
• Form spores	• Water needed for fertilisation		
• Water needed for fertilisation			

Flowering plants are also divided into **monocotyledons** (grasses, some flowering plants) and **dicotyledons** (trees and shrubs) according to whether they have one or two **cotyledons** (the first leaves) in the seed. Monocots usually have long narrow leaves with parallel veins; dicots usually have broad leaves with branching leaf veins.

Animalia

This is the biggest kingdom. Animals eat other living organisms so they can usually move and find food. They are multicellular. Their cells do not have cell walls, and usually have nuclei. The classification of animals is complicated. A simplified version is shown in the diagram. The different phyla of animals are described below.

Annelida

These are **worms**. They have long cylindrical bodies divided into segments. Each segment has bristles called **chaetae** which help in movement (see page 113).

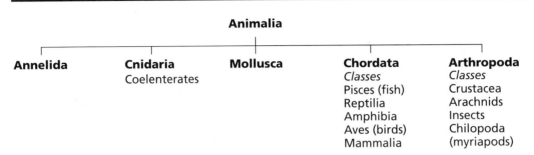

Classification of the Animalia kingdom

Molluscs

Molluscs include snails, slugs, mussels, whelks, oysters, squid and octopuses (strange but true!). Many (but not all) molluscs have a hard shell which is either a single coil (snail) or in two halves (bivalve), which can be opened and closed. Squid have a plate-like structure inside their bodies. Molluscs also have a muscular foot, which in octopuses and squid is the set of tentacles. Snails and slugs have a simple lung for breathing; the other molluscs have gills.

Arthropods

The **arthropods** include **spiders**, **insects** and **crustaceans**, and are the biggest phylum of animals. They all have the following features:

- no spine (**invertebrates**)

- jointed legs (arthropod means jointed limb)

- waterproof **exoskeleton** (**cuticle**)

- a body divided into segments with joints between for movement.

Crustacea include crabs, lobsters and woodlice. They breathe through gills, so they usually live in wet places, and have at least four pairs of jointed legs and two pairs of **antennae** which are sensitive to chemicals and light. They also have **compound eyes**, which are made up of lots of separate lenses with light-sensitive cells underneath. These form a crude image and are very sensitive to movement.

Arachnids include spiders, scorpions and ticks. Their bodies are divided into two segments: the **cephalothorax** (head and thorax) and abdomen. They have four pairs of jointed legs on the cephalothorax. They do not have antennae but do have a pair of **chelicerae** to hold the prey. They breathe through gills called **book lungs.** They have several pairs of **simple eyes**.

Insects have three pairs of jointed legs, two pairs of wings (which may be vestigial) and one pair of antennae. Their bodies are divided into three segments (head, thorax and abdomen). They breathe through tracheae.

Chilopoda are centipedes and millipedes. They are made up of lots of segments with a pair of appendages on each segment. (They are also called **myriapods**.) They have one pair of antennae, and simple eyes.

Chordata

Chordata are all **vertebrates**: they have a spine (back bone). The distinguishing features of each class are shown in the table opposite.

Pisces	Amphibia	Reptilia	Aves	Mammalia
Fish	*Frogs, toads, newts*	*Snakes, lizards, turtles*	*Birds*	*Mammals*
• Live in water	• Adults live on land; **larvae (tadpoles)** in water	• Live on land	• Feathers	• Skin covered with hair or fur
• Fins	• Adults have 4 limbs	• Breed on land	• 4 limbs; forelimbs are wings	• 4 limbs
• Skin covered in scales	• Breed in water; eggs fertilised externally	• Dry scaly skin	• Legs are scaly and have claws	• Eggs fertilised internally
• Breathe through gills	• Moist skin; no scales	• 4 limbs with toes (other than snakes)	• Beak	• Placenta
• Eggs fertilised in water	• Adults have lungs; larvae have gills	• Eggs fertilised internally	• Eggs fertilised internally	• Fully formed young born
• Poikilothermic	• Poikilothermic	• Eggs have waterproof shells	• Eggs have hard shells	• Young suckled from mammary glands
• **Bony** fish have a bone skeleton, a swim bladder to control depth and a gill flap (**operculum**)		• Poikilothermic	• Homeothermic	• Homeothermic
• **Cartilaginous** fish have a cartilage skeleton, no swim bladder, use fins to control depth, do not have an operculum				• Diaphragm and lungs
				• Heart has 4 chambers
				• Different types of teeth
				• Well developed cerebral hemispheres

Dichotomous keys

This is a way of classifying organisms. At each stage you have two possibilities which help you to identify what type of organism you have or what group or subgroup it belongs to. A very simple example is shown below.

1. Has roots.. **2**
   Has rhizoids...................................... **Bryophyte**

2. Produces spore................................. **Filicinophyte**
   Produces seed.................................... **3**

3. Seeds develop in cones..................... **Coniferophyte**
   Seeds develop in fruit....................... **Angiospermophyte**

A simple dichotomous key for plants

Distribution of organisms

Animals or plants live where there is a suitable **environment. Environmental factors,** such as cold or wet, affect where an organism can survive. Many organisms have special **adaptations** to cope with environmental factors (see below). Environmental factors affect the **distribution** of organisms, their size, ability to reproduce, and population. **Predation** and **competition** also affect the distribution and relative abundance of different organisms in a habitat.

Environmental factors

Biotic factors are the influences of other living things. These include availability of food and water, **pathogens, predators** and competition for food and shelter.

Abiotic factors are non-living influences. These include the **climate** (sun, temperature, rainfall) and chemical and physical factors: the levels of nutrients, oxygen or pollutants, the pH of soil or water, etc. Factors caused by the soil are called **edaphic** factors.

Adaptation

We already know that organisms have to be adapted to their environment in order to survive. There are lots of examples of adaptation in biology. We just have to know about a few.

Polar bears live in the Arctic where it is below freezing for most of the year. They have the following adaptations:

- white fur for **camouflage** against snow

- thick fur to **insulate** against heat loss on land

- a thick layer of **blubber** to insulate against heat loss in water

- hairy pads on their feet to help with walking on ice
- powerful forelimbs for movement on land and for swimming
- large claws for hunting
- good eyesight and sense of smell for hunting
- a large surface area to volume ratio, to decrease energy loss
- can eat plants if meat (seals, fish and walruses) isn't available.

Camels live in **arid** desert areas where it is very hot and there is little water. They have the following adaptations.

- The nostrils are narrow slits lined with hair to trap dust and sand; they can be closed.
- The eyes are protected from sand by thick eyelashes.
- The feet are splayed out and have leathery soles to make walking on soft shifting sand easy.
- The body is covered with fur, which protects against loss and gain of heat.
- A large surface area to volume ratio decreases energy loss.
- Water can be stored in the stomach; camels can drink vast amounts of water when they get the chance.
- Fat is stored in the hump and serves as a food store from which water is released during metabolism.
- The body tissues can withstand extremes of temperature. (It is usually cold at night in the desert.)
- The body tissues can tolerate dehydration (the body fluids get more concentrated as water is lost).
- Heat can be lost by sweating if the camel has enough water.

Predation

Animals that eat other animals are called **predators** and their food is called **prey**. Predators are adapted for catching and killing; prey are adapted to protect themselves from being caught or eaten. For example, caddis fly larvae, which are eaten by dragon fly nymphs, camouflage themselves using a case made of leaves. Owls are adapted for hunting: they have very good eyesight and hearing, and can fly very quietly so that mice and small rodents don't hear them coming.

Plants protect themselves from being eaten by herbivores by having thorns, spines, stings (e.g. the stinging nettle) or by releasing a toxin. For example, ragwort is poisonous to cattle.

Predators are one of the factors that affect the population of an organism. Sometimes predators are introduced on purpose by man to control the population of a pest (see page 128).

Competition

Organisms can compete with each other for food, water, shelter, etc. Competition can be between members of the same species, or between different species that live in the same habitat. Animals that have overlapping niches (life-styles) compete for some of the things that they need; the less overlap between the niches, the less competition there is. If they compete for all aspects of their niche, eventually one species will oust the other. Competition controls the populations of the species: if one of the competing species is destroyed for some reason, the other can flourish.

Metamorphosis

Insects reduce competition by **metamorphosis**: the eggs hatch into larvae – grubs, maggots or caterpillars – which eat and grow very quickly. The larvae then have a **dormant** stage during which they change into the adult insect. Because the young and adults are very different, they do not compete for food. For example, blowfly larvae feed on rotting meat, whereas the adult blowfly feeds on carbohydrate-rich foods. The young and adults also have different functions: the larvae is growing, it has all the food it needs and so doesn't need to be mobile; the adult needs to be able to find food, a mate, and somewhere to lay the eggs. It therefore needs wings so it can move around. The metamorphosis of the blowfly is shown in the diagram.

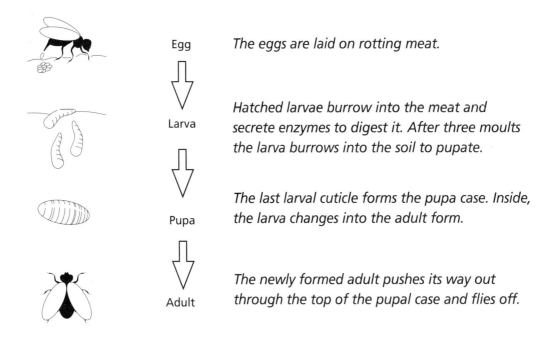

Egg — *The eggs are laid on rotting meat.*

Larva — *Hatched larvae burrow into the meat and secrete enzymes to digest it. After three moults the larva burrows into the soil to pupate.*

Pupa — *The last larval cuticle forms the pupa case. Inside, the larva changes into the adult form.*

Adult — *The newly formed adult pushes its way out through the top of the pupal case and flies off.*

Complete metamorphosis of the blowfly

This is an example of **complete metamorphosis**. Some insects like locusts and dragonfly undergo **incomplete metamorphosis**: they hatch as **nymphs** rather than larvae and with each **moult** the nymph becomes a bit more like the adult. It doesn't go through the resting pupa stage.

Population size

Population size is controlled mostly by birth rate and death rate (although people or organisms migrating in or out of a population also have an effect on its size). Usually, the *average* population of an organism stays fairly constant over a period of time, although it may fluctuate from one year to the next. For example, if the population of greenfly is particularly large one year, the population of ladybirds (which eat greenfly) is also likely to increase (because more food is available), but will decrease again when the number of greenfly decreases (usually because they have been eaten by all the extra ladybirds).

If the birth rate and death rate are equal, the population stays a constant size. Populations grow when the birth rate is higher than the death rate, which is what is happening with the human population.

Animals that are prey to other animals usually produce large numbers of young in the hope that a proportion will survive to reproduce. (This is why so many greenfly are produced, yet their population stays fairly constant over all.)

When an organism reaches a new environment, the population increases rapidly but soon levels off as an environmental factor comes into play to control the size of the population. (Availability of food is usually the main factor, although disease or predation could also be important.)

Managing populations

Farming involves developing an artificial ecosystem and managing it carefully so that crops survive and grow. Predators have to be kept under control, competition from weeds is prevented using herbicides, and competition between crop plants is prevented by ensuring that plants are not planted too close together.

Fish farming

This is another example of an artificial, managed ecosystem. Trout or salmon are raised in ponds containing freshwater that has been diverted from a river. The water that is returned to the river (the **effluent**) contains faeces and uneaten food from the ponds and a lot of the oxygen has been removed. It is vital that the population of farmed fish and their food supply are strictly managed, otherwise the effluent could cause pollution and eutrophication (see page 126). One way to avoid this is to pass the effluent through settling tanks so that the organic matter is filtered out.

One concern with managed fish is that, because there are so many similar fish in a small area, disease can spread rapidly. Farmers use a chemical called **dichlorvos** to control fish lice, but this is toxic to crustacea and molluscs. A more 'eco-friendly' approach is biological control: other fish – **wrasse** – are raised with the salmon and pick the lice off their bodies. Some farmers also put antibiotics in the water to prevent disease. This is not very good practice because it encourages antibiotic-resistant bacteria (see page 144) to flourish, and the antibiotic could get passed on to humans, causing a similar problem.

There is also a concern that farmed fish could escape and interbreed with wild fish, passing on characteristics that compromise their ability to survive.

Fishing

Fish is a key source of protein. However, in the last few years there has been a lot of concern about **over-fishing**: the number of fish being removed from the population by fishing is more than can be replaced by breeding. This means that fish stocks are dwindling.

One way of preventing this has been to introduce fishing quotas, or total allowable catches – fishing fleets are told how many fish they are allowed to catch in a certain period of time. Some areas have a 'closed season' when fishing isn't allowed, so that fish stocks can build up again. This system is used in the halibut fishing industry in the Pacific. Another approach is to fix the size of the mesh in fishing nets so that immature fish can escape and grow on.

It is difficult to estimate the size of a fish population, and therefore decide how many fish can be caught without affecting the overall population over several years – this is the **maximum sustainable yield**.

Many people are dependent on fishing for food and livelihood. It is therefore important that fish stocks are protected in the long term, but without damaging people's livelihoods.

Worked questions

Q1.

		Dog-like animals	Horse-like animals
	Genus	*Canis*	*Equus*
	Species	Domestic dog: *familiaris*	Pony: *callabus*
		Wolf: *lupus*	Zebra: *burchelli*
		Fox: *mesomeles*	

Use the table above to work out the Latin name for a) the zebra b) the fox c) the domestic dog.

A1. a) Zebra = *Equus burchelli*

b) Fox = *Canis mesomeles*

c) Domestic dog = *Canis familiaris*

Q2. *List the five kingdoms in binomial classification.*

A2. Bacteria
Protoctists
Fungi
Plantae
Animalia

Q3. *List three differences between bryophyta and coniferophyta.*

A3. a) Bryophyta form spores, coniferophyta produce seeds.

b) Bryophyta don't have a xylem or phloem whereas coniferophyta do.

c) Bryophyta have to live in water, coniferophyta can live on land.

Q4. *What are the distinguishing features of arthropods?*

A4. They are invertebrates (i.e. no spine); they have jointed legs; they have a waterproof exoskeleton, and their bodies are divided into segments.

Q5. *Give four distinguishing features of mammals.*

A5. i) The skin is covered with hair or fur.

ii) They give birth to fully formed young.

iii) They have a diaphragm and lungs.

iv) The young are suckled from mammary glands.

(NB There are many more differences – see page 151.)

Q6. *Briefly describe an example of a complete metamorphosis. What advantage does metamorphosis provide?*

A6. The blowfly is an example of a complete metamorphosis. The eggs are laid in rotting meat, where they hatch into larvae. The larvae feed on the rotting meat and grow and moult. After the third moult they go into a dormant phase (the pupa) in which they change into the adult form.

Metamorphosis provides an organism with a competitive advantage. The young and adults are different forms and eat different foods. They don't compete for food, which increases their chances of survival.

topic eighteen
microorganisms in health and disease

Diseases

- **Infectious diseases** are caused by living organisms called **pathogens** – bacteria, viruses*, fungi or protoctists. Tuberculosis, AIDS, malaria, diphtheria, athlete's foot and flu (influenza) are just a few examples of infectious diseases. Food poisoning is also caused by a pathogen. (*Viruses are not technically living organisms; see page 159.)

- **Inherited diseases** are caused by genes (e.g. sickle cell anaemia or cystic fibrosis).

- **Autoimmune diseases** occur when the immune system gets confused and attacks the body's own cells. Some types of arthritis and diabetes are autoimmune diseases.

- **Degenerative diseases** like heart disease and some types of arthritis are the result of natural ageing.

- **Deficiencies** are caused by a lack of something in the diet, usually a mineral or vitamin (see topic four).

- Some diseases are **'self-inflicted'**. For example smoking can cause heart disease and cancer.

Any disease that is not caused by a pathogen is **non-infectious**.

Pathogens

The pathogens get into the body and breed. Sometimes they feed on body cells, or sometimes they release a toxic waste product (a **toxin**) which causes symptoms like a rash or a high temperature.

Pathogens get into the body in different ways. Diseases that are easily passed from one person to another are said to be **highly infectious** – flu is an example.

- Some bacteria and viruses (e.g. the one that causes warts) can get through the skin; others get in through cuts or wounds.

- Viruses are often carried in the air in tiny droplets of moisture, which are released when somebody with the virus sneezes or speaks, and are then breathed in by other people.

- Some bacteria are carried in water (e.g. Cholera), which is why it is so important that drinking water is kept clean, or food (e.g. Salmonella).

- Some diseases are carried from one host organism to another by a **vector**. Mosquitoes are vectors for the malaria pathogen (a protoctist), which gets into the blood when the mosquito bites.

Viruses

Influenza (flu) is caused by a virus, which is breathed in. The virus gets into your cells and hijacks the 'machinery', instructing it to make lots more viruses. These new viruses burst out of the cell, infecting more cells, and so on. (Some are breathed out, which is why flu is so infectious.)

Once your body realises that it is infected, the immune system kicks in and starts to get rid of the virus. This is when you start to get the symptoms. The period between breathing the virus in and getting the symptoms is called the **incubation period**. You don't know that you are infected, but you can infect other people during this period. Although the symptoms make you feel pretty dreadful, the immune system is working at this stage, and symptoms like high temperature are all part of the campaign to get rid of the virus.

The common cold is also caused by a virus. However, the cold virus keeps changing the proteins in its outer coat, which means that your immune system won't recognise it. Cold viruses are carried in the air, and are released when you sneeze. Basic hygiene, such as using disposable tissues and washing your hands can help stop the spread of the virus.

(Viruses are not really living organisms because they cannot survive on their own, and they don't respire or grow. They are packets of DNA or RNA in a protein coat.)

Cholera

Cholera is caused by a bacterium called ***Vibrio cholerae*** which lives in water. It is spread very quickly if drinking water is not kept clean. If the faeces from an infected person get into water that is used for drinking or washing food, the bacterium is passed on to other people.

The incubation period is only a few days and then the person becomes very ill. The bacteria produce a toxin that affects the immune system, causing very bad diarrhoea. Lots of water is lost from the body, and if the person doesn't take lots of fluid (**rehydration**), they can die of **dehydration**. Rehydration therapy also has glucose and salts in it, to help absorb water from the intestine into the blood.

Although cholera is rare in Britain, **epidemics** can occur in developing countries if water gets contaminated.

Amoebic dysentery

This is caused by a protoctist called ***Entamoeba histolytica***, which lives and breeds in the large intestine and damages the lining of the colon. It causes pain in the abdomen, blood in the faeces, and sometimes bad diarrhoea. However, some people are infected with the protoctist without having any symptoms.

The disease is spread by **cysts**, which are living *E. histolytica* surrounded by a protective coat. If faeces from an infected person get into drinking water, the cysts can then infect other people.

(If you use the Latin name for an organism several times, write the full name out the first time, then you can abbreviate the genus for the rest of the time.)

Malaria

Malaria is caused by the protoctist **Plasmodium**, which is carried from host to host by female mosquitoes of the genus **Anopheles**. The mosquito sucks up blood through a proboscis but to stop the blood clotting, she injects some saliva. If the saliva contains *Plasmodium*, this gets injected too. *Plasmodium* infects liver cells where it breeds and then infects red blood cells, where it can breed even faster. The bursting of red blood cells as the viruses are released causes the symptoms of malaria, particularly a high temperature. The burst cells can block blood vessels, affecting blood supply to different parts of the body.

Malaria is difficult to control. One way is to kill the mosquitoes that act as vectors. However, in many places the mosquitoes have become resistant to the insecticides that have been used. You can also use mosquito nets and insect-repellent creams so that you don't get bitten by the mosquitoes. Another way is to get rid of areas of stagnant water where mosquitoes lay their eggs, stopping them from breeding. Making sure that there is no uncovered water also helps, as does spraying the surface of water with oil so that the larvae can't get to the surface to get oxygen.

Drugs can be used to kill *Plasmodium* if you get infected (or as a precaution if you are bitten by a mosquito) or to prevent you getting infected. Unfortunately, many *Plasmodia* are now resistant to these drugs so new ones are needed. Scientists are also trying to develop a vaccine for malaria.

Athlete's foot

This is caused by a fungus called **Tinea**. Mild athlete's foot is quite common. It usually occurs between the toes and makes the skin flake and crack. It can cause quite bad skin damage if it spreads. It can be spread in communal showers and swimming pools, and thrives on sweaty feet. (It is described as **contagious** because it is spread by touch.)

You can reduce the risk of catching athlete's foot by **disinfecting** communal areas (chlorine in swimming pools is a disinfectant), and by making sure that you wash and dry your feet properly, change your socks regularly, and wear shoes that allow your feet to 'breathe'.

AIDS

Autoimmune deficiency syndrome (which is what AIDS stands for) is caused by a virus called **HIV (human immunodeficiency virus)**. It infects lymphocytes (particularly T cells), gradually destroying them over a long period of time. This means that an infected person becomes less able to fight off other infections. After many years of being infected with HIV, the person develops the symptoms of AIDS. They are very vulnerable to infection, and often get cancer (because one of the jobs of the immune system is to destroy cells that cause cancer).

HIV is transmitted by *direct contact* of body fluids. This can happen during sex, and can be prevented by using a condom. It is also transmitted by blood. This means that people like doctors, nurses and ambulance attendants who deal with accidents must wear protective clothing so that they do not accidentally come into contact with infected blood. Drug users who share hypodermic needles are also at risk of getting infected with HIV.

HIV is actually quite fragile (unlike the tough cold virus). It can't be spread by sneezing or physical contact. In fact, you are more of a risk to someone with HIV than they are to you because you might pass on a pathogen that their immune system will have problems dealing with.

Parasites

Parasites live in close association with another organism (the **host**), usually causing them harm.

Tapeworms, which live inside the alimentary canal, and the protoctist *Plasmodium*, which causes malaria, are called **endoparasites** because they live inside the host. **Head lice** are called **ectoparasites** because they live on the outside of the host.

Eggs are eaten by cattle. The eggs hatch into embryos in the alimentary canal.

The embryo bores through the wall of the alimentary canal and lodges itself in a muscle. It develops into a **bladder worm**.

Proglottids – segments of the body – full of eggs fall off and are egested in the faeces.

Humans eat the infected muscle (meat). The young tapeworm attaches to the alimentary canal and grows.

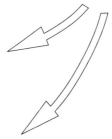

If the infected meat is destroyed, or if it is cooked thoroughly to destroy the embryos, the life cycle is broken.

*This is the life cycle of the tapeworm. The human is the **primary host**; the cattle (pig or cow) is the **secondary host**. Parasites sometimes use a secondary host as a vector to ensure that the offspring survive.*

The tapeworm grips tightly onto the wall of the alimentary canal by hooks and suckers. It also has a covering that is resistant to the digestive enzymes. People become infected with tapeworms by eating infected pork or beef (see diagram). In Britain meat is carefully inspected for bladder worms and any that is infected can't be sold. This has broken the life cycle of the tapeworm, gradually **eradicating** it.

Head lice are also well adapted to their parasitic lifestyle. They are flat so that they can lie against the scalp, and the eggs are firmly cemented onto the hair. The adults' legs grip the hair very tightly so that they are not brushed off. Lice get from one head to the next when heads are in close contact or by sharing hair brushes or combs. They are easily killed by using a special lotion on the head and hair, which kills the adults and the eggs.

Controlling disease

Sterilisation

Infectious germs can be removed by **sterilising**, which is done either by heating objects to a high temperature in a pressure cooker or autoclave, or by using a chemical disinfectant. A germ-free environment (like a hospital operating theatre) is **aseptic**.

Antiseptics

Antiseptics are also chemicals that are used to kill germs. For example, if you cut yourself, an antiseptic can be used to make sure that the wound doesn't get infected.

Antiseptics were discovered by Lister in the 1860s. He realised that many patients died after surgery from gangrene caused by a bacterial infection. He sprayed the wound with carbolic acid to prevent it going septic.

Antibiotics

Antibiotics are substances that kill bacteria (but not viruses) without affecting living cells. They are made by fungi (which would compete with the bacteria for food). We have exploited this to develop antibiotics for use in humans. Penicillin was the first antibiotic discovered. It stops bacteria from manufacturing cell walls. Other antibiotics have also been developed.

(Penicillin was discovered by Alexander Fleming. He noticed that some of his bacterial cultures didn't grow if they were infected with mould; the mould was producing something that killed the bacteria. He isolated the substance and called it penicillin after the Penicillium *mould that made it.*

Florey and Chain later found ways of extracting penicillin from mould so that it could be used to treat infections. It was particularly valuable in the Second World War, stopping gangrene and blood poisoning.)

Commercial production of penicillin

Penicillin is produced by fungi of the genus *Penicillium*. Different strains are used to produce different types of penicillin. These can also be modified chemically to make them more effective.

Penicillin is produced in huge fermenting tanks (which can be up to 100 000 litres). The tanks provide the conditions that the fungi need to proliferate.

(Fermentation is a process in which a microorganism uses an external energy source to obtain energy; this changes the medium they are in.)

- The source of carbohydrate is sugar, usually lactose or 'corn steep liquor', which is a by-product of cornflour production.

- The nutrient solution also contains amino acids and minerals.

- The pH is kept between 5 and 6.

- The temperature is kept at 26°C.

- Air is blown through the liquid to provide oxygen.

- The solution is stirred all the time.

- Everything is sterile so that unwanted microorganisms don't get in and disrupt the system.

The nutrient liquid is seeded with the fungi, which are then allowed to grow. As the nutrient supply decreases, the fungi secrete the antibiotic into the medium. The liquid can then be run off and the penicillin is extracted.

Antibiotic resistance

A big problem is that bacteria become resistant to antibiotics like penicillin (see page 144). This means that doctors have to be very careful to use antibiotics only when they know that they are needed. (For example, sore throats are usually caused by viruses, so there is no point in taking an antibiotic.)

Immunisation

One of the jobs of your immune system is to provide **immunity** (see page 65). This means that if you encounter a pathogen for the second time, your immune system immediately springs into action so that the pathogen is dealt with before it causes an infection and makes you ill. This is why you get illnesses like measles only once. This is called **natural active immunity**.

Natural immunity is also passed on from mother to baby. Antibodies from the mother pass across the placenta into the baby's blood while it is growing. The mother's milk also contains antibodies, which help the baby fight off infection while it is being breast fed. This is called **passive immunity**. It doesn't last long because the antibodies soon disappear, but it does help the baby while its own immune system develops.

Vaccines provide you with **artificial active immunity**. They stimulate your body to produce antibodies against the pathogen. Different types of vaccine are used.

- You can be vaccinated with live pathogen which has been bred so that it doesn't actually give you the disease. Tuberculosis and rubella vaccines are in this form.

- You can be vaccinated with killed pathogen (e.g. whooping cough).

- Toxins produced by bacteria can act as antigens that stimulate the immune system. An altered version of the toxin that doesn't make you ill can be used as a vaccine (e.g. diphtheria).

- Sometimes, just the part of the virus that acts as the antigen is used as the vaccine (e.g. flu or hepatitis B), in which the vaccine contains part of the virus's protein coat.

Vaccines can also provide you with **artificial passive immunity**, if you think you might have been infected. For example, the **antitetanus** jab contains antibodies to help fight off the tetanus bacterium. The antibodies are produced by injecting a weakened form of the virus into a horse. The antibodies are then separated from the blood and used for the jab. The antibodies don't stay in your blood for very long, but hopefully for long enough to fight the infection. You can also have a vaccination against tetanus, in which you are injected with a weakened form of the virus so that you make your own antibodies.

Vaccines can be very good at preventing the spread of diseases. However, sometimes a vaccine can cause side-effects. For example, the whooping cough vaccine caused headache and fever in some children and occasionally caused brain damage. Parents have to decide which is the greater risk: dying from whooping cough if their child is not vaccinated, or the very slight chance of brain damage if they are vaccinated.

Girls are usually vaccinated against rubella (German measles). Although it is not a serious illness, if a pregnant woman comes into contact with the virus, there is a high risk that the baby's nervous system will be damaged, and the baby may be born deaf or blind.

(Edward Jenner discovered the smallpox vaccine. He noticed that milk maids who caught cowpox from cows, rarely caught the more serious [usually fatal] illness, smallpox. During a smallpox outbreak, he deliberately infected some of his patients with cowpox, and none of them got smallpox. He also showed that pus from smallpox sores did not cause smallpox in a boy who had recovered from cowpox. His work led to the development of a vaccine for smallpox; this disease has now almost been eradicated.

Louis Pasteur showed that diseases were caused by microbes. He found that the microbe that caused chicken cholera was weakened if it was left exposed to the air for some time. When he injected the weakened microbe into chickens, they were immune to the disease. He had discovered a vaccine. He went on to produce vaccines for anthrax and rabies.)

Microorganisms and food

Microorganisms can cause food to go bad. *Mucor* is a common mould that grows on bread. The tips of the hyphae secrete enzymes which digest the bread into sugars, amino acids and fats that can be taken up by the mould.

As well as digesting food, fungi and bacteria can produce substances that make the food smell and taste bad (which does at least stop you eating it) and can also produce toxins that cause food poisoning. The bacterium *Salmonella* is a common cause of food poisoning. It is found in raw meat but is killed during cooking.

Chickens are frequently infected with *Salmonella* if they are farmed intensively. The crowding of the chickens means that it is spread easily. Although the chickens are not affected by the bacteria living in their gut, carcasses can be contaminated by bacteria from the gut and skin. Keeping chicken houses free of faeces would help stop the bacteria spreading.

You can get *Salmonella* poisoning by eating chicken that has not been cooked properly. It is important that chicken is thawed completely before it is cooked, otherwise the inside doesn't get hot enough to kill the bacteria, even though the outside is cooked. If food that is not going to be cooked comes into contact with raw meat that is infected with *Salmonella*, the bacteria can be transferred and multiply. This is why it is important to keep cooked and raw foods completely separate in the fridge.

The bacteria release an **endotoxin** (a poison) which inflames the lining of the small intestine, causing fever, vomiting and diarrhoea.

Food hygiene

It is important to make sure that you don't spread germs to food. It is also important to bear in mind that bacteria multiply only very slowly in cool temperatures (e.g. in the fridge) and much more quickly at warm temperatures (10–48°C). Most bacteria are killed at temperatures above 65°C if they are exposed for long enough and are killed very quickly at 120°C.

- Wash your hands before handling food, and avoid sneezing, coughing or smoking over it.
- Keep animals away from food.
- Cover food to keep flies off; their feet and saliva can carry bacteria.
- Keep raw meat away from cooked foods.
- Scrub chopping boards and utensils (and hands) that come into contact with raw meat.
- Make sure that food is cooked properly and is piping hot in the middle.
- Thaw meat properly before cooking it.

- Avoid reheating food because bacteria can grow in the warm temperatures while food cools and heats. You should cool or heat food quickly to minimise this possibility, and make sure that it is piping hot when reheated.

- Don't refreeze food that has thawed. Bacteria can multiply in food while it is thawing, and then carry on multiplying when it is thawed a second time. The bacteria are not killed by freezing.

- Keep food in the fridge. Bacteria can multiply only very slowly at this temperature.

Preserving food

Food that needs to be kept for some time needs to be **preserved** to stop microorganisms growing. There are lots of ways of doing this, these are just some of them.

- **Freezing**: the food is cooled quickly to –15°C to prevent dehydration. Microorganisms can't grow at this temperature.

- **Canning**: the food is boiled to kill the microorganisms and sealed in cans (tins) to prevent entry of new ones. Vegetables, meat and fruit can be stored in this way. The boiling process destroys the vitamins in canned fruit and vegetables.

- **Drying**: the food (flour, fruit, vegetables, sometimes meat) is dried in air in an oven until the water content is very low. Microorganisms can't grow without water.

- **Ultra heat treatment (UHT)**: steam at 160°C is blown through milk to destroy the microorganisms.

- **Salting**: the food (meat or vegetables) is soaked in concentrated sodium chloride (salt), which is too concentrated for microorganisms to grow in.

- **Irradiation**: this is quite a new way of preserving food in which **gamma irradiation** is used to destroy bacteria so that it keeps longer. Irradiation doesn't destroy toxins, however, so it must be done before any are produced. Some people are concerned that radiation is left in the food, or that vitamins in the food are destroyed by this process. Irradiation is the only way of making chicken completely free of *Salmonella*.

- **Chemicals**: so-called 'E-numbers' are used to preserve food. However, these can cause side-effects in some people.

Using microorganisms in food production

Although microorganisms can make food go bad, they are also used to produce some foods.

Yeast

Yeast is a single-celled fungus. If it is added to a sugar solution, it uses the sugar for anaerobic respiration in which it converts the sugar to ethanol (alcohol) and carbon dioxide. This process is **alcoholic fermentation** (see page 48). Beer is made by providing the yeast with maltose from germinating barley seeds. Wine is made by providing the yeast with sugar from grapes. *Saccharomyces cerevisiae* is the yeast most frequently used in wine and beer making.

When yeast respires aerobically, carbon dioxide is released. This is used for bread making. The dough is made from flour and water. The flour contains starch (the energy source for the yeast), **amylase** (which breaks down the starch into sugar) and protein, particularly **gluten**, which forms sticky threads as the yeast works on the dough, trapping the carbon dioxide that is produced as bubbles. The trapped gas makes the bread rise. The yeast and alcohol that is formed are destroyed when the bread is baked.

Lactobacillus

These are bacteria used to make cheese and yoghurt. Species of *Streptococcus* are also used. The bacteria respire anaerobically when provided with lactose (in milk) as a source of sugar. Lactic acid is produced, which lowers the pH of the milk, making the protein (**casein**) coagulate into clumps called **curds** and a liquid called **whey**. **Rennet**, which is a mixture of enzymes including **chymosin**, is also added. This also acts on the milk protein to make it coagulate even more. The curds and whey are separated, and the curds are pressed to make cheese.

Different cheeses are made by using different milk, different strains and combinations of *Lactobacillus*, letting the bacteria work for different lengths of time or at different temperatures, letting the cheese ripen for different lengths of time, etc. Fungi may also be added to produce blue cheese. The veins in cheese like Stilton are the hyphae of the fungi. Holes are made so that the fungi get enough oxygen.

Yoghurt is also produced from milk but using a mixture of *S. thermophillus* and a different strain of *Lactobacillus: L. balgaricus*. A culture of the bacteria is added to warm milk and left for a few hours at 46°C. Usually, the milk is heated to 70°C first to destroy unwanted bacteria (this is **pasteurisation**), then the *Lactobacillus* is added.

Single cell protein

We can use microorganisms themselves as a source of food, particularly in areas of the world where there is a shortage of protein-rich food. Microorganisms do not need soil to grow in, and can be grown from lots of different food sources, some of which are very cheap to produce. Microorganisms are lower down the food chain (see page 117) than meat, so less energy is wasted.

Mycoprotein is a single cell protein made from a fungus called *Fusarium* (which is made from hyphae rather than single cells). It is grown in large fermenters, using carbohydrate left over from flour-making as the food source. Other nutrients like ammonium nitrate are also added. The *Fusarium* reproduces quickly and makes a mass of mycelium, which is harvested. The RNA is removed and the protein dried and shaped into chunks. It is quite bland in taste but has a texture similar to meat. It is very high in protein (45%) and fibre, but has very little fat and no carbohydrate, so it is a healthy source of protein that is cheap to produce. (Quorn® is mycoprotein.)

Genetic engineering

Genetic engineering is the process of taking a gene for a particular protein from one organism and putting it into another organism. For example, the gene for human insulin is inserted into the bacterium *Escherichia coli*. The *E. coli* then make human insulin, which can be used to treat diabetes. Human growth hormone and Factor VIII (for treating people with haemophilia) can also be made in this way.

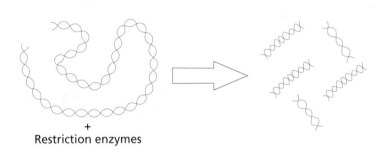

+
Restriction enzymes

*a) The DNA is extracted from cells and chopped up into bits by **restriction enzymes**. The bit of DNA for the protein you want to produce (the gene) can then be isolated.*

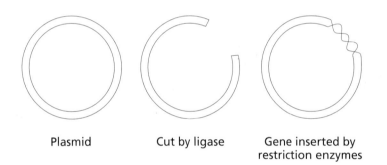

Plasmid   Cut by ligase   Gene inserted by restriction enzymes

*b) The gene is inserted into a **plasmid**. This is a ring of DNA that can reproduce itself inside living cells. It acts as a **vector**, carrying the gene into the bacterium. The plasmid is cut open by a restriction enzyme and the gene is fixed in place by **ligase enzymes**.*

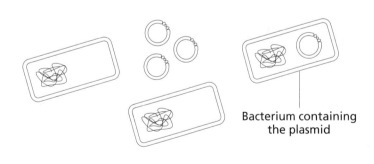

Bacterium containing the plasmid

c) The plasmids are added to a culture of the bacterium. Some of them are taken into bacteria. The bacteria that contain plasmids are separated from the rest and cultured in a big vat.

Fermentation broth contains bacteria and the protein you want to make. (Obviously you can't really see them!)

d) The bacteria make the wanted protein using the instructions in the inserted DNA and secrete it into the fermentation broth. The protein is separated and purified for use.

Genetic engineering in food production

There are lots of ways of using genetic engineering to produce or improve food. Enzymes used in the production of food can be made by genetic engineering. Rennin is usually extracted from the stomachs of calves, but this is no good for vegetarians. The rennin produced by genetic engineering can be used to make cheese that is suitable for vegetarians.

Genes can be inserted into organisms other than bacteria. For example, tomatoes can have an extra gene added that controls ripening so that they can be stored for longer. A variety with improved flavour has also been produced. Strains of soya beans have been genetically engineered to flourish in temperate climates, and so that they grow to the right height for mechanical harvesting so that none is wasted.

Genes that make plants resistant to herbicides can also be added so that a crop can be sprayed with the herbicide to kill the weeds, without damaging the crop. Another idea is to add a gene that makes the plant repellant to insects so that it is not eaten.

Some people are concerned that genetic engineering may not be safe because bacteria and viruses with extra genes are being produced. Although these are not pathogenic microorganisms, people are concerned about what might happen if they mutated and became pathogenic. There are strict regulations about the types of genes and microorganisms that can be used for genetic engineering.

People are also concerned that herbicide resistance in crops could be passed to weeds so that they also become resistant. A similar problem could happen if a gene for insect resistance got transferred to wild plants. Insects wouldn't be able to eat the plants, which could upset a whole ecosystem.

Worked questions

Q1. What is the difference between infectious and non-infectious diseases. Give two examples of each and say what they are caused by.

A1. Infectious diseases are caused by pathogens – other living organisms such as bacteria, viruses and fungi. Examples are influenza, which is caused by a virus, and athlete's foot, which is caused by a fungus.

Non-infectious diseases are not caused by pathogens. Examples are diabetes, which is an autoimmune disease, and cystic fibrosis, which is genetic.

Q2. What causes malaria and how is it transmitted?

A2. Malaria is caused by a protoctist called *Plasmodium*. It is carried by female mosquitoes of the genus *Anopheles*. When the mosquito bites, it injects saliva to stop the blood clotting and the *Plasmodium* is also injected.

Q3. What is HIV? How is it transmitted?

A3. HIV is human immunodeficiency virus – the virus that causes AIDS. It is transmitted by direct contact of body fluids such as blood or semen.

Q4. What is a parasite? Give two examples.

A4. A parasite is an organism that lives on or in another organism – its host. It usually harms the host. Examples are the tapeworm and head lice.

Q5. What is the difference between an antiseptic and an antibiotic?

A5. An antiseptic is a chemical that kills all microbes; an antibiotic only kills bacteria.

Q6. Why do we need to be careful about using antibiotics?

A6. Bacteria can mutate so that they become resistant to a particular antibiotic. If that antibiotic is used, the resistant bacteria can survive and flourish, whereas the non-resistant ones are all killed. This means that there are more and more resistant bacteria, which are difficult to kill with antibiotics.

Q7. What type of immunity is provided by vaccines? How do vaccines work?

A7. Vaccines provide artificial active immunity. The vaccine contains dead pathogen or live pathogen that has been treated so that it doesn't make you ill. The vaccine stimulates your body to produce antibodies and memory cells. If you come into contact with the pathogen, your body can quickly mount an immune reaction so that the pathogen is killed before it makes you ill.

Q8. Why should chicken be thawed completely before cooking?

A8. Chicken can contain *Salmonella* bacteria which cause food poisoning. If chicken is cooked from frozen, the meat may get warm enough for the bacteria to multiply, but not hot enough to kill them.

Q9. Give two examples of organisms used in food production and what they are used for.

A9. Yeast is used in bread making and to brew beer. Bacteria of the genus *Lactobacillus* are used to make cheese and yoghurt.

Q10. What are plasmids? How are they used in genetic engineering?

A10. Plasmids are loops of genetic material (DNA or RNA) that can reproduce themselves in living cells. They are used as vectors to carry the gene for the protein that you want to produce into the host, which is usually a bacterium.

appendix

Hints and tips

1. Read and re-read the question. Look for the *meaning* of the question carefully by finding *key words*. It may help you to underline the key words. Make sure you have answered the question fully.

2. As soon as you read the question, try to think of all the *key points* that go with the topic.

3. Write *legibly*; the examiner is not going to give you the benefit of the doubt for something s/he can't read.

4. The examiners mark to *very strict mark schemes*. They are looking for key words or phrases. Being aware of this allows you to make concise answers. Don't waffle; make your point(s) *clearly* and *concisely*. The mark scheme will tell you how many points the examiner is looking for. Always give a few extra points, in case some of your other points didn't win you a mark.

5. If you get stuck on a question, move on. In most cases, if you start doing the questions you can do, picking up the easy marks, you'll regain your confidence. Then you may well be able to have a stab at the hard question.

6. *Pace yourself.* Don't go too fast, you'll make silly mistakes. Don't go too slowly, because you won't finish. Leave yourself enough time at the end to check your answers.

7. When you check, you should effectively do the question again. Try covering up your first answer with your hand. Don't assume that your first answer was wrong, though.

8. Don't worry.

9. Be happy.

10. Relax.

11. Be confident.

12. Smile (and the world smiles with you).

13. And above all, BE PREPARED.

14. This isn't a hint but I didn't want to end on 13 in case some of you are superstitious.

So, best of luck to all of you. I know what GCSEs are like; I went through them.

GOOD LUCK!

index